Compendium of Learning and Development Quizzes

Compendium of
Learning and Development Quizzes

Sarah Cook

GOWER

Published by
Gower Publishing Limited
Gower House
Croft Road
Aldershot
Hants GU11 3HR
England

Gower
Suite 420
101 Cherry Street
Burlington, VT 05401-4405 USA

Sarah Cook has asserted her right under the Copyright, Designs
and Patents Act 1988 to be identified as the author of this book.

British Library Cataloguing in Publication Data

Cook, Sarah, 1995–
    Compendium of learning and development quizzes
    1. Executives - Training of 2. Management - Problems,
    exercises, etc.
    I. Title
    658.4'07124

Library of Congress Cataloging-in-Publication Data

Cook, Sarah, 1955–
    Compendium of learning and development quizzes/Sarah Cook
        p.cm.
    Includes bibliographical references.
    ISBN 0-566-08540-2 (alk. paper)
    1. Employees--training of--Examinations, questions, etc.
    2. Executives--Training of--Examinations, questions, etc. 3.
    Organizational learning--Examinations, questions, etc.
    4. Leadership--Examinations, questions, etc. I. Title.

    HF5549.5.T7C59547 2002
    658.3'124--dc21

                                        2003048311

ISBN 0 566 08540 2

Typeset in Palatino and Helvetica by LaserScript Ltd, Mitcham, Surrey
Printed and bound in Great Britain by MPG Books Ltd, Bodmin, Cornwall

Contents

Preface

This compendium came about as the result of my experiences as a management development consultant running Stairway Consultancy. In designing and facilitating learning interventions, I often encounter occasions when an alternative medium of increasing self-awareness, assessing or consolidating learning is appropriate.

OBJECTIVES OF THE COMPENDIUM

The compendium is intended to provide trainers, HR professionals, line managers and team leaders with a selection of management development quizzes. It is designed to be part of a trainer's toolkit and deliberately covers a range of topic areas. I have personally designed and tested the quizzes in a wide variety of development situations.

DESIGN OF THE COMPENDIUM

The quizzes are displayed in alphabetical order, according to topic heading. For ease of use I have grouped them into nine topic areas:

- Communication skills
- Customer service
- Health and safety
- Leadership
- Performance management
- Personal development
- Team work
- Recruitment and selection
- Training and development

There is a range of quizzes in each category. The Matrix on the following pages displays these. The majority of quizzes are followed by suggested answers, detailing the proposed responses to the questions plus additional recommended reading.

WAYS OF USING THE MATERIAL

The quizzes in this compendium are not designed to 'test' individuals in the negative sense of the word. Rather they are intended to provide the learner with an opportunity to:

- Reflect on their own thinking on the topic area
- Identify knowledge, skills or behavioural gaps and thereby assess learning and development needs
- Encourage self-awareness
- Encourage group discussion
- Consolidate learning

Most quizzes work best when they are included as part of a training and development programme. However, they work equally well as part of one-to-one training or coaching sessions. They can be used:

- As preparatory material before a development session to help individuals assess their knowledge, skills, attitude or approach towards a topic
- During a development session – either as an individual assessment tool at the beginning of or during the intervention or as a means of generating group discussion during the session. Alternatively you can also use them as a way of consolidating learning, such as during a learning review
- As follow-up material to help individuals reflect on what they have learned from the session

When using the quizzes it is helpful to describe fully their purpose before they are issued. Also, unless you wish to use the quiz as a basis for group discussion, it is best practice to indicate to participants that the results of the quizzes will not be shared.

If you decide to use the results as the basis for group discussion, remember to give participants the option or not of sharing their results. This helps ensure that people do not feel 'put on the spot'.

Completing a quiz provides people with an opportunity to assess and reflect on their behaviour. Remember to allow sufficient time for this. Also it is best to be familiar with the material by undertaking the quiz as a pilot yourself before issuing it widely.

Many quizzes include or lend themselves to the development of an action plan following their completion.

All quizzes can be adapted to meet the needs of the individuals within the group by changing wording, phrases or questions to suit the organisation for which the quiz is intended.

ACKNOWLEDGEMENT OF SOURCES

I have developed many of the quizzes over my years of working as a development consultant. I am indebted to the numerous management development trainers and management development thinkers who have inspired me to develop this collection.

I hope that you find this a useful, informative and valuable training aid.

Sarah Cook
sarah@thestairway.co.uk

MATRIX	Communication skills	Customer service	Health and safety	Leadership	Performance management	Personal development	Team work	Recruitment and selection	Training and development
1 Action centred leadership				X					
2 Assertiveness	X			X		X			
3 Body language	X			X					X
4 Coaching skills				X					X
5 Coaching styles				X					X
6 Conflict management		X		X		X			
7 Counselling skills				X					X
8 Creative problem solving				X		X			
9 Customer care		X							
10 Disciplinary and grievance interviews					X				
11 Delegation				X					
12 Diversity				X				X	
13 Emotional intelligence	X	X		X		X			
14 Empowerment		X					X		
15 Facilitation skills	X								X
16 Feedback skills				X	X				
17 Handling difficult customer situations	X								
18 Health and safety			X						
19 Induction						X		X	
20 Influencing skills	X			X					
21 Leadership styles				X					
22 Learning styles						X			X

MATRIX	Communi-cation skills	Customer service	Health and safety	Leadership	Performance management	Personal development	Team work	Recruitment and selection	Training and development
23 Listening skills	X				X	X			
24 Managing change				X		X			
25 Meeting skills				X		X	X		
26 Mentoring skills				X					X
27 Motivating others				X	X	X	X		
28 Negotiation skills				X		X			
29 One-to-one training									X
30 Performance appraisal					X				
31 Performance appraisal – before, during and after					X				
32 Interviewing poor performers					X				
33 Presentation skills						X			X
34 Project management				X		X			
35 Questioning skills	X								
36 Recruitment and equal opportunities								X	
37 Recruitment interviewing								X	
38 Recruitment and selection									
39 SMART objectives					X				
40 Stress management						X			
41 Team work							X		
42 Telephone skills	X								
43 Time management						X			
44 Written communication skills	X								

1
Action centred leadership

Use this quiz to help individuals identify the actions that an effective leader will take in the areas of:

- Satisfying the needs of the task
- Satisfying the needs of the team
- Satisfying the needs of individuals

Action centred leadership

Below is a list of activities that managers undertake. Identify for each statement whether the manager is:

- Satisfying the needs of the task
- Satisfying the needs of the team
- Satisfying the needs of individuals

When they are doing this activity:

1 Define, discuss, agree and write down objectives and targets

2 Tell the group about its tasks and the reasons for them

3 Clearly divide up and delegate tasks; define them, allocate them according to skills, training and inclinations

4 Identify team strengths and weaknesses and therefore training needs

5 Display the team's objectives and targets to all and obtain agreement to all

6 Clarify procedures, rules and policies

7 Set standards to work to

8 Hold social events

9 Involve the team in decision making

10 Set up systems and timescales and maintain task timing

11 Conduct one-on-one discussions to identify specific skills and knowledge, clarify roles and responsibilities, set objectives/targets/standards to work to

12 Identify each person's strengths and areas for improvement

13 Listen and ask for ideas

14 Offer feedback/praise/recognition

15 Identify motivators

16 Monitor progress of task

17 Adjust plans and workload when necessary

18 Monitor internal and external influences which may affect the progress of the task; and communicate them to others as necessary

19 Evaluate results

20 Review what needs to be changed for the future

21 Maintain business awareness

22 Conduct team meetings to give and receive information, get ideas, give praise and feedback

23 Make decisions

24 Set ground rules

25 Maintain harmony in the team, resolve conflict

26 Co-ordinate and guide the team, rather than adopt a 'hands on' approach

27 Discuss career development opportunities

28 Clarify roles and responsibilities, set objectives/targets/standards to work to

Suggested answers

Here are the suggested answers. In many cases the manager satisfies more than one need.

1 Define, discuss, agree and write down objectives and targets: **Task**

2 Tell the group about its tasks and the reasons for them: **Team**

3 Clearly divide up and delegate tasks; define them, allocate them according to skills, training and inclinations: **Team and Individual**

4 Identify team strengths and weaknesses and therefore training needs: **Team**

5 Display the team's objectives and targets to all and obtain agreement to them: **Team**

6 Clarify procedures, rules and policies: **Task**

7 Set standards to work to: **Task**

8 Hold social events: **Team**

9 Involve the team in decision making: **Team**

10 Set up systems and timescales and maintain task timing: **Task**

11 Conduct one-on-one discussions to identify specific skills and knowledge: **Individual**

12 Identify each person's strengths and areas for improvement: **Individual**

13 Listen and ask for ideas: **Team and Individual**

14 Offer feedback/praise/recognition: **Team and Individual**

15 Identify motivators: **Individual**

16 Monitor progress of task: **Task**

17 Adjust plans and workload when necessary: **Task**

18 Monitor internal and external influences which may affect the progress of the task and communicate them to others as necessary: **Task**

19 Evaluate results: **Task**

20 Review what needs to be changed for the future: **Task**

21 Maintain business awareness: **Task**

22 Conduct team meetings to give and receive information, get ideas, give praise and feedback: **Team**

23 Make decisions: **Task**

24 Set ground rules: **Task and Team**

25 Maintain harmony in the team, resolve conflict: **Team**

26 Co-ordinate and guide the team, rather than adopt a 'hands on' approach: **Team**

27 Discuss career development opportunities: **Individual**

28 Clarify roles and responsibilities, set objectives/targets/standards to work to: **Individual**

Recommended reading

Adair, John (1979) *Action Centred Leadership*, Gower Publishing, Aldershot.

2
Assertiveness

This quiz is designed to help identify the differences between assertive, aggressive and passive-aggressive behaviour.

Assertiveness

Look at each of the situations below and assess whether the response is assertive, aggressive, passive or passive-aggressive. Where the response is not assertive, write in an alternative reply which is assertive.

Situation	Response	Assertive? Passive? Aggressive? Passive-aggressive?	Alternative assertive response (if original response not assertive)
1 Your manager has been out of the office for the past three days. You have a number of issues that you need to raise with him urgently on his return. When he returns, he goes straight to his desk and says that he does not want to be disturbed.	'I know that you are busy, but I do need to speak to you urgently. If now is not convenient, what time today would be?'		
2 A colleague arrives 30 minutes late for an important 9.00 a.m. meeting that you are also attending. They were responsible for the first item on the agenda. You say:	'Good afternoon!'		
3 It is 5.00 p.m. and your manager gives you a piece of work that she needs completed straight away. You know that it will take at least two hours to complete. You have plans for this evening and have already told your boss that you needed to leave by 5.30 p.m. You say:	'Well, I suppose I can do it.'		
4 You have bought an electrical item which is faulty and you take it back to the shop. You say:	'Give me my money back or I'll report you to Trading Standards!'		

Situation	Response	Assertive? Passive? Aggressive? Passive-aggressive?	Alternative assertive response (if original response not assertive)
5 One of your customers insists that you deliver their order straight away. You know that the consignment will not all be ready until tomorrow. You say:	'I appreciate that you need the delivery urgently. The complete consignment will not be ready until tomorrow, but I can arrange for two-thirds to be delivered today. Will that be acceptable?'		
6 You are in a review meeting with your manager. You would really like to attend French language classes to help you deal with French clients. When you ask your boss he says: 'You don't need to do that, you're fine as you are.' You say:	'Oh, OK, if you think so.'		
7 A colleague in another team has volunteered your services to her manager without consulting you. The next time you see your colleague you say:	'What do you think you're playing at? You've no right to offer my services without asking me!'		
8 You are issuing tickets to a queue of customers, when suddenly one customer pushes himself to the front and asks: 'I need to have my ticket now. Do you know who I am?!' You reply:	'Does anyone know who this person is, he appears to have forgotten his name?'		

Suggested answers

Situation 1 = Assertive
Situation 2 = Passive-aggressive
Situation 3 = Passive
Situation 4 = Aggressive
Situation 5 = Assertive
Situation 6 = Passive
Situation 7 = Aggressive
Situation 8 = Passive-aggressive

Definitions

Assertive behaviour

People using assertive behaviour clearly express that both they and the other person have rights and needs. Their behaviour is open and respectful.

Passive behaviour

People using passive behaviour express that others' rights and needs have precedence over their own. Onlookers can perceive this behaviour as timid, inhibited and self-denying.

Aggressive behaviour

People who use aggressive behaviour boldly insist that their rights and needs prevail. Their behaviour can be seen as domineering, pushy and self-centred.

Passive-aggressive behaviour

People who use passive-aggressive behaviour subtly make sure that their rights and needs prevail. Their behaviour can be perceived as sarcastic, underhand and manipulative.

Recommended reading

Ash, Eve and Quarry, Peter (1999) *Assertiveness Skills Indicator*, Gower Publishing, Aldershot.
Back, Kate and Back, Ken (1982) *Assertiveness at Work*, McGraw-Hill, Maidenhead.
Eggert, Max A. (1997) *Assertiveness Pocketbook*, Management Pocketbooks, London.
Gillen, Terry (1997) *Assertiveness for Managers*, Gower Publishing, Aldershot.

3
Body language

This is a quiz that is designed to be 'acted out' – that is, individuals are given different roles to play non-verbally. The quiz element lies in the rest of the group interpreting successfully the body language.

4
Coaching skills

This quiz is designed to test people's understanding of the best way to coach individuals.

Coaching skills

Look at the following questions and statements and identify which approaches an effective coach would use:

At the beginning of the coaching session

1 a) 'What you need to do is improve your influencing skills.'
  b) 'I understand that you want to improve your influencing skills, is that correct?'
  c) 'What would you like to achieve from this session?'

2 a) 'What makes you think that you can't influence effectively now?'
  b) 'What specific aspects of your influencing skills do you want to improve?'
  c) 'I can see why you might have problems in this area.'

3 a) 'What's happening now when you try to influence people?'
  b) 'What approaches have you tried in the past?'
  c) 'When was the last time you failed to influence someone?'

During the middle of the coaching session

4 a) 'What I suggest you do then is be less forceful in your views.'
  b) 'How do you think you can improve your influencing skills?'
  c) 'I had the same problem and in my experience it's best to listen more and talk less.'

5 a) 'What options have you got?'
  b) 'Who do you think is an effective influencer in the media; what do you think they do?'
  c) 'What other routes might there be to improving?'

6 a) 'Which option seems most achievable?'
  b) 'You need to start doing something about this straight away.'
  c) 'In my opinion the only way to do it is to talk to her in person.'

At the end of the coaching session

7 a) 'What are you going to do in order to go forward?'
  b) 'What are the next steps for you?'
  c) 'When you speak to her you need to tell her exactly how you feel.'

8 a) 'When will you take this action?'
   b) 'What's wrong with seeing her this week?'
   c) 'I suggest that you see her this week.'

9 a) 'What support do you need in achieving this?'
   b) 'When will you know if you've been successful?'
   c) 'Come back to me as soon as you have seen her and let me know the outcome.'

Suggested answers

At the beginning of the coaching session

1 c) 'What would you like to achieve from this session?'

The objectives of the session should be driven by the coachee, not the coach.

2 b) 'What specific aspects of your influencing skills do you want to improve?'

The coachee's objectives should be as specific as possible.

3 a) 'What's happening now when you try to influence people?'
   b) 'What approaches have you tried in the past?'

A discussion should take place around the coachee's current and past approaches to the situation. The language used by the coach should be positive, e.g. not 'failed to influence'.

During the middle of the coaching session

4 b) 'How do you think you can improve your influencing skills?'

The coach should encourage the coachee to think of their own solutions.

5 a) 'What options have you got?'
   c) 'What other routes might there be to improving?'

The coach should encourage the coachee to explore all options.

6 a) 'Which option seems most achievable?'

The coach should help the coachee select the options that seem most realistic and achievable to them.

At the end of the coaching session

7 a) 'What are you going to do in order to go forward?'
   b) 'What are the next steps for you?'

The coachee needs to determine and be committed to the action.

8 a) 'When will you take this action?'

The coach should encourage the coachee to set their own timescales.

9 a) 'What support do you need in achieving this?'
  b) 'When will you know if you've been successful?'

The coach should help the coachee determine the support they need and the criteria for success. These should not be imposed by the coach.

Recommended reading

Macheman, Nigel (1995) *Coaching and Mentoring*, Gower Publishing, Aldershot.
Whitmore, John (2002) *Coaching for Performance*, Nicholas Brealey Publishing, London.

5
Coaching styles

This quiz is designed to help people appreciate the three styles of coaching and when it is most appropriate to use them.

Coaching styles

Directing coaching style

The coach retains control.

The coach sets objectives with the coachee, provides solutions and gives clear and detailed instructions on what to do.

The coach works closely with the coachee in implementing the solution, checking their understanding and giving feedback on progress.

A directing coaching style works well when:

Guiding coaching style

The coach retains some control, but allows the coachee as much freedom as they feel comfortable with.

The coach sets objectives with the coachee, they discuss and explore issues with the coachee.

The coach helps the coachee to evaluate options for development. The coach adds their suggestion as one of those options.

The coach tends to only get involved with the coachee at their request.

A guiding coaching style will work well when:

Enabling coaching style

The coach helps the coachee to manage their own learning.

The coach will typically use questions to help the coachee think things through for themselves.

The coach encourages the coachee to develop their own solutions and ways forward.

The coach acts as a sounding board for coachees and reviews their experiences with them.

An enabling coaching style will work well when:

Suggested answers

Directing coaching style works well when:

The coachee lacks confidence and competence

They are new to the job or task and have no experience in this area

They are new to the role and have no previous experience in this area

Guiding coaching style works well when:

The coachee lacks competence but is confident

The coachee lacks confidence but is competent

The coachee has not undertaken the specific task before, but may have experience of similar tasks

The coachee has not undertaken the specific role before but may have experience of similar roles

Enabling coaching style works well when:

The coachee is competent and confident

The coachee has undertaken the specific task before

The coachee has undertaken the specific role before

Recommended reading

Whitmore, John (2002) *Coaching for Performance*, Nicholas Brealey Publishing, London.

6
Conflict management

This quiz allows people to identify the most effective style of conflict management.

Conflict management

There are four approaches that you can adopt when dealing with conflict:

HIGH	**COMPETITION** I boldly insist that my rights and needs prevail	**NEGOTIATION** I clearly express that we both have equal rights and needs
Satisfying own needs		
LOW	**AVOIDANCE** I do not express my own needs and I ignore the needs of others	**COMPLIANCE** Others' rights and needs take precedence over mine
	LOW HIGH	

Satisfying the needs of others

Read each situation below, then assign one of the four conflict management styles to each response.

1 Someone disagrees strongly with you about something that really matters to you at work. You:

   a) Walk away rather than express your views
   b) Express your opinions in as strong a fashion as the other person
   c) Soothe their feelings rather than start an argument
   d) Listen to what they have to say and state your feelings in a rational manner

2 You are negotiating with someone over a price. They refuse to bring the price down. You:

   a) Tell them what you are willing to pay and say that's final
   b) Accept the price they offer
   c) Let someone else do the talking
   d) Question the price and seek a more favourable exchange

3 Someone who works for you has not performed a task to the standard that you were expecting. You:

   a) Mention it in a roundabout way so as not to hurt their feelings
   b) Put off telling the person
   c) Tell them directly and forcibly what they have not done
   d) Ask them the reason for the performance shortfall, explain the consequence of this and how you would like things to change

4 Conflict has arisen in your team. You:

   a) Help the team find a compromise solution
   b) Do not say anything during the team meeting
   c) Concur with the majority view
   d) Put your point across strongly

5 Your boss gives you some feedback on something he believes you did wrong. You react by:

   a) Shrugging your shoulders and walking away
   b) Agreeing with him that it was wrong
   c) Telling him loudly that you disagree
   d) Asking him for reasons why he thinks this was wrong

6 You have been waiting in a queue for 20 minutes and someone in front of you butts in. You:

   a) Say: Go away! You've got a cheek!
   b) I have been waiting here 20 minutes, please don't butt in
   c) If you really need to be in front of me, that's OK
   d) Let them take the place in front of you

Suggested answers

1 Someone disagrees strongly with you about something that really matters to you at work. You:

   a) Walk away rather than express your views – **Avoidance**
   b) Express your opinions in as strong a fashion as the other person – **Competition**
   c) Soothe their feelings rather than start an argument – **Compliance**
   d) Listen to what they have to say and state your feelings in a rational manner – **Negotiation**

2 You are negotiating with someone over a price. They refuse to bring the price down. You:

   a) Tell them what you are willing to pay and say that's final – **Competition**
   b) Accept the price they offer – **Compliance**
   c) Let someone else do the talking – **Competition**
   d) Question the price and seek a more favourable exchange – **Negotiation**

3 Someone who works for you has not performed a task to the standard that you were expecting. You:

   a) Mention it in a roundabout way so as not to hurt their feelings – **Compliance**
   b) Put off telling the person – **Avoidance**
   c) Tell them directly and forcibly what they have not done – **Competition**
   d) Ask them the reason for the performance shortfall, explain the consequence of this and how you would like things to change – **Negotiation**

4 Conflict has arisen in your team. You:

   a) Help the team find a compromise solution – **Negotiation**
   b) Do not say anything during the team meeting – **Avoidance**
   c) Concur with the majority view – **Compliance**
   d) Put your point across strongly – **Competition**

5 Your boss gives you some feedback on something he believes you did wrong. You react by:

   a) Shrugging your shoulders and walking away – **Avoidance**
   b) Agreeing with him that it was wrong – **Compliance**
   c) Telling him loudly that you disagree – **Competition**
   d) Asking him for reasons why he thinks this was wrong – **Negotiation**

6 You have been waiting in a queue for 20 minutes and someone in front of you butts in. You:

   a) Say: Go away! You've got a cheek! – **Competition**
   b) I have been waiting here 20 minutes, please don't butt in – **Negotiation**
   c) If you're in a rush and you really need to be in front of me, that's OK – **Compliance**
   d) Let them take the place in front of you – **Avoidance**

Recommended reading

Lacey, Hoda (2000) *How to Resolve Conflict in the Workplace*, Gower Publishing, Aldershot.

Markham, Ursula (1993) *How to Deal with Difficult People*, HarperCollins, London.

7
Counselling skills

This quiz is designed to help individuals recognise the skills they need to be effective counsellors.

Counselling skills

Below are five different situations that you may face where counselling is required. Imagine that one of your team has come to you with the issue described in the relevant scenario. Tick the response that you believe best matches a counselling style.

Situation A

'When I took on the job I was told that people could be flexible with their hours. It's not easy having to work overtime because I have to pick up the kids. I can't always rely on my childminder to work overtime too.'

1 Tell me what arrangements you have with your childminder. Does she work only certain hours?
2 As you have children, you are responsible for collecting them at certain times so it's not easy to stay late, is that what you're saying?
3 You must feel pulled in two directions. Perhaps you've not made it clear that you have to leave on time because of your commitments?
4 It sounds really difficult to manage. There must be other ways round this. Why not change your childminder or join an after-school club?
5 Well, I'll see what I can do to help. Perhaps Petra from the other section could take on some of your work. Do you want me to ask her?

Situation B

'I've now had a chance during my traineeship to see all of the departments in the company. I've decided that I'm not happy in the work I'm doing. I don't think I'm suited for this kind of job. I'd far rather start again in an area which will give me more job satisfaction.'

1 So you feel you'd be a lot happier if you could start out afresh in a new area, is that it?
2 Whether this is the right job for you, who can say, but it's good you've come to a decision.
3 Are you sure you are making the right decision? It seems a pity to waste the time you've already spent in the business.
4 So you've decided you'd be better off leaving?
5 How much have you looked into other possible areas of work?

Situation C

'Well, I really thought that I had the job in the bag. It's just not on. I'm far better qualified than him and I've been with the company a longer time. If he thinks he can come in here and tell me what to do, he's another think coming.'

1 So you feel you're much better than him and you wouldn't like it if he were your boss?
2 Well, you may be better qualified, but do you think the head of department would have chosen him if he didn't seem right?
3 Yes, that will be very difficult. When is he likely to take on the job?
4 So you really don't want to work for him?
5 Hold on, don't jump the gun. Why do you think that he will tell you what to do?

Situation D

'I don't know if I can take any more. I've had angry customers on the phone ranting and raving that they haven't received their goods. The people in the transport department don't help. They don't even answer their phones. It's all right for them, they don't have to deal with members of the public.'

1 It's no use blaming another department. It's part of your job to deal with customer concerns. It's something you just have to get used to.
2 I know it's not easy, but you get used to dealing with angry people after a while. It will seem much better tomorrow.
3 So what exactly is the problem customers are experiencing?
4 Maybe transport are so snowed under with work they can't answer their phones.
5 So it seems as though everyone has been giving you a hard time today and it's difficult to take.

Situation E

'I know it's no use. Whatever I say he's not going to believe me because I'm not his blue-eyed boy. He's already told the others that my productivity is down. Just because I'm less experienced than them doesn't mean I can't do as good a job.'

1 You're getting this out of proportion. Could it be because you feel you were passed over for promotion?
2 I know, he can be a pain sometimes. If I were you, I wouldn't take any notice of it.
3 What else has happened in the past to suggest he doesn't like you?
4 If I understand you correctly, you feel he won't take your word about it and that he's trying to undermine your confidence.
5 It isn't fair. You should let his manager know about this. I'll come with you if you like.

Suggested answers

The following responses represent a non-evaluative counselling style:

Situation A

2 As you have children, you are responsible for collecting them at certain times so it's not easy to stay late, is that what you're saying?

Situation B

4 So you've decided you'd be better off leaving?

Situation C

1 So you feel you're much better than him and you wouldn't like it if he were your boss?

Situation D

5 So it seems as though everyone has been giving you a hard time today and it's difficult to take.

Situation E

4 If I understand you correctly, you feel he won't take your word about it and that he's trying to undermine your confidence.

Recommended reading

MacLennan, Nigel (1996) *Counselling for Managers*, Gower Publishing, Aldershot.
Redman, Warren (1995) *Counselling Your Staff*, Kogan Page, London.

8
Creative problem solving

This is a fun quiz to help people recognise the stages of creative problem solving and problem solving techniques.

Creative problem solving

Discover the mystery word related to creativity by taking the appropriate letter of the correct answers to the following questions:

1 The first letter of the mystery word is the first letter of the word that describes the obstacles to creativity (8 letter word)

2 The second letter of the mystery word is the second letter of the words describing what should happen with ideas when you are generating them (5 and 9 letter words)

3 The third letter of the mystery word is the third letter of the word that describes what you should not do when generating ideas (8 letter word)

4 The fourth letter of the mystery word begins the first word of the first stage of the creative problem solving process (8 letter word, 3 letter word, 7 letter word)

5 The fifth letter of the mystery word is the fifth letter of the name of the creative writer who wrote about 'Six thinking hats' (2 letter word and 4 letter word)

6 The sixth letter of the mystery word is the third letter of the response to the question: 'Can anyone be creative?'

7 The seventh letter of the mystery word is the first letter of the four word phrase that is sometimes used to describe the creative process (8 letters, 7 letters, 3 letters, 3 letters)

8 The eighth letter of the mystery word is the ninth letter of the four word phrase that can sometimes be used to describe the creative process (8 letters, 7 letters, 3 letters, 3 letters)

9 The ninth letter of the mystery word is the same as the second letter of the mystery word

10 The tenth letter of the mystery word is the second letter of the fourth stage of the problem solving process (9 letter word, 3 letter word, 8 letter word)

Mystery word:

__ __ __ __ __ __ __ __ __ __
1   2   3   4   5   6   7   8   9   10

Note: Take the first letter from your answer to Question 1; the second letter from your answer to Question 2 and so on.

Ideal answer

1 The first letter of the mystery word is the first letter of the word that describes the obstacles to creativity (8 letter word) = **B**ARRIERS

2 The second letter of the mystery word is the second letter of the words describing what should happen with ideas when you are generating them (5 and 9 letter words) = C**R**OSS-FERTILISE

3 The third letter of the mystery word is the third letter of the word that describes what you should not do when generating ideas (8 letter word) = EV**A**LUATE

4 The fourth letter of the mystery word begins the first word of the first stage of the creative problem solving process (8 letter word, 3 letter word, 7 letter word) = **I**DENTIFY THE PROBLEM

5 The fifth letter of the mystery word is the fifth letter of the name of the creative writer who wrote about 'Six thinking hats' (2 letter word and 4 letter word) = DE BO**N**O

6 The sixth letter of the mystery word is the third letter of the response to the question: 'Can anyone be creative?' = YE**S**

7 The seventh letter of the mystery word is the first letter of the four word phrase that is sometimes used to describe the creative process (8 letters, 7 letters, 3 letters, 3 letters) = **T**HINKING OUTSIDE THE BOX

8 The eighth letter of the mystery word is the ninth letter of the four word phrase that can sometimes be used to describe the creative process (8 letters, 7 letters, 3 letters, 3 letters) = THINKING **O**UTSIDE THE BOX

9 The ninth letter of the mystery word is the same as the second letter of the mystery word = **R**

10 The tenth letter of the mystery word is the second letter of the fourth stage of the problem solving process (9 letter word, 3 letter word, 8 letter word) = I**M**PLEMENT THE SOLUTION

THE MYSTERY WORD IS: **BRAINSTORM**

Recommended reading

Proctor, Tony (1999) *Creative Problem Solving for Managers*, Routledge, London.
Robson, Mike (2002) *Problem Solving in Groups*, third edition, Gower Publishing, Aldershot.

9 Customer care

This quiz is designed to be used at the start of or during a customer care programme.

Customer care quiz

Each space identifies something about the people on this course. Seek out your fellow participants and if one of the listed items applies to them, ask them to sign their name in the appropriate place. They can only sign their names once.

When you get three complete lines (up or down), shout out that you have finished!

Has external customer contact in their job	Has had a good customer experience in the past week – (say who with)	Has made a complaint as a customer to another organisation in the past month	Is a customer of yours	Talks to customers on the phone every day
Feels confident dealing with difficult customers	Has received great service at Disneyland	Has attended a customer or employee focus group	Has recognised a colleague for excellent service in the past month	Knows three regular customers by name – state who these are
Can name two excellent service organisations	Has put customer service on a meeting agenda in the past month	Has improved a process in the past six months to better satisfy their customer	Is a customer of Tesco	Uses the products and services of your organisation
Has attended a seminar on customer service before today	Has answered a complaint letter from a customer in the past month	Has received a compliment from a customer in the past month	Provides a service to you	Deals with customer feedback

Recommended reading

Cook, Sarah (2001) *Customer Care Excellence*, Kogan Page, London.

10
Delegation

This quiz encourages individuals to consider the best way to delegate and their approach to delegation.

Delegation

Select the best of the alternatives given for each question.

1 The main reason why managers fail to delegate more is:

    a) They feel they can do the jobs better than their subordinates
    b) They do not have sufficient confidence in their subordinates
    c) It is quicker to do the jobs themselves

2 When delegating a task the manager delegates:

    a) Responsibility for the task
    b) Accountability
    c) Responsibility and authority

3 When delegating a task to someone you should:

    a) Involve him/her in the process of delegation
    b) Give clear, precise details about how you want the task done

4 When you have a task delegated to you must:

    a) Listen carefully and follow instructions
    b) Ask questions to establish exactly what is expected

5 When you have delegated a task to someone you should:

    a) Agree when this will be reviewed
    b) Let them get on with it
    c) Monitor their progress at regular intervals

6 People develop more when tasks are delegated to them and when:

    a) They are told in detail how to complete the task
    b) They receive help in achieving the task
    c) They are allowed to make and learn from their mistakes

7 If someone delegates a task upwards this is a sign that:

    a) The person is a poor time manager
    b) The person concerned needs training in this area
    c) The manager is not providing sufficient supervision

8 When you receive work which has been delegated to you by two different people you should:

    a) Make each person aware of the other tasks that have been delegated to you
    b) Decide which tasks are the most important and concentrate on these

Suggested answers

1 The main reason why managers fail to delegate more is:

   c) It is quicker to do the jobs themselves

In thinking that it is quicker to do the job themselves, managers fail to realise that delegating saves time in the long run. It is also the main means managers have of developing their team.

2 When delegating a task the manager delegates:

   a) Responsibility for the task

The manager delegates responsibility for the task but is still accountable for its completion.

3 When delegating a task to someone you should:

   a) Involve him/her in the process of delegation

By involving the person to whom you are delegating a task, you establish the extent of the guidance that you need to give them to help them achieve the task. It could be that the person to whom you are delegating the task has ideas and suggestions of their own to add.

4 When you have a task delegated to you must:

   b) Ask questions to establish exactly what is expected

The person to whom a task is delegated needs to ask questions to establish exactly what is expected. The person delegating should also make a point of asking the person to whom they are delegating for questions so that the task is clear.

5 When you have delegated a task to someone you should:

   a) Agree when this will be reviewed

Different people need different levels of supervision. Always agree when the task will be reviewed.

6 People develop more when tasks are delegated to them and when:

   c) They are allowed to make and learn from their mistakes

People learn best when they are allowed to try things out. This means that mistakes may occur. However, people learn from their mistakes.

7 If someone delegates a task upwards this is a sign that:

   b) The person concerned needs training in this area

It is important before delegating a task to someone that they are trained in the skills and knowledge to complete the task effectively.

8 When you receive work that has been delegated to you by two different people you should:

  a) Make each person aware of the other tasks that have been delegated to you

It is the responsibility of the person delegating the task as well as the person to whom the task has been delegated to ensure that each knows what other work the person has to accomplish.

Recommended reading

Smart, J.K. (2002) *Real Delegation*, Prentice Hall, London.

11
Disciplinary and grievance interviews

This quiz helps individuals assess their approach to disciplinary and grievance interviews. The information on the right to be accompanied relates to Sections 10–15 of the Employment Relations Act 1999 which came into force on 4 September 2000.

Disciplinary and grievance interviews

Answer the questions below to assess your understanding of disciplinary and grievance interviews.

1 What is a disciplinary interview?

2 Which of the following could be the cause of a disciplinary interview?

   • A worker caught stealing from the company
   • A worker who has performed consistently badly against objectives
   • A worker who has breached their terms of employment by giving confidential information to a competitor

3 What is a grievance interview?

4 Which of the following could be the cause of a grievance interview?

   • Harassment and bullying
   • Issues of equal pay
   • A dispute about a pay rise

5 When can a worker be accompanied to a disciplinary or grievance interview?

6 If a worker asks to be accompanied to the disciplinary or grievance interview, does the worker have to be employed by the company or can they be casual, temporary or agency workers too?

7 If the worker is accompanied, who can this companion be?

8 What does the manager need to do to ensure the grievance or disciplinary interview is effective?

9 What is the consequence if the employer has failed or threatened to fail to comply with the worker's rights to be accompanied?

10 What is the consequence if the employer subsequently dismisses both the worker and their companion for exercising their rights?

Suggested answers

1 What is a disciplinary interview?

A disciplinary interview is a hearing that could result in:

- The administration of a formal warning to a worker
- The taking of some other action in respect of a worker
- The confirmation of a warning issued or some other action taken

2 Which of the following could be the cause of a disciplinary interview?

- A worker caught stealing from the company
- A worker who has performed consistently badly against objectives
- A worker who has breached their terms of employment by giving confidential information to a competitor

All could be the cause of a disciplinary hearing

3 What is a grievance interview?

A grievance interview is a hearing which concerns the performance of a duty by an employer in relation to a worker. It also covers grievances rising out of day-to-day friction between fellow workers which, if reported to management, impose a duty on the employer to take some action.

4 Which of the following could be the cause of a grievance interview?

- Harassment and bullying
- Issues of equal pay

A dispute about a pay rise could not be the cause of a grievance hearing as employers do not have a legal obligation to award pay rises.

5 When can a worker be accompanied to a disciplinary or grievance interview?

- When a worker is required or invited by his or her employer to attend a disciplinary or grievance hearing
- When the worker reasonably requests to be accompanied at the interview
- The right does not apply when the interview is initiated by the worker

6 If a worker asks to be accompanied to the disciplinary or grievance interview, does the worker have to be employed by the company or can they be casual, temporary or agency workers too?

The worker has the right to be accompanied irrespective of whether they are employed, casual, temporary or agency workers.

7 If the worker is accompanied, who can this companion be?

- Someone who is chosen by the worker
- A fellow worker
- A trade union official or a lay official

8 What does the manager need to do to ensure the grievance or disciplinary interview is effective?

- Familiarise themselves with the organisational disciplinary or grievance procedure. Preferably talk this through beforehand and be accompanied by a member of the HR team
- Collect relevant evidence before the hearing
- Keep to a structure during the interview
- Stay calm and do not argue
- Be clear of the outcome of the interview
- Ensure notes are taken during the meeting (by the HR representative)

9 What is the consequence if the employer has failed or threatens to fail to comply with the worker's rights to be accompanied?

A worker can complain to an employment tribunal who, if they find the employer liable, will fine against them. A failure to allow a worker to be accompanied where the worker is then dismissed in practice will make a case of unfair dismissal likely.

10 What is the consequence if the employer subsequently dismisses both the worker and their companion for exercising their rights?

The dismissal is automatically considered unfair.

Recommended reading

ACAS Code of Practice Disciplinary & Grievance Procedures (2002), The Stationery Office Books, London.

Everson, Colin (2002) *How to Avoid Employment Tribunals*, Gower Publishing, Aldershot.

12
Diversity

This quiz encourages managers to identify what they can do to encourage diversity in the workplace.

Diversity

It is envisaged that by December 2003 government directives will be in place to tackle discrimination in employment and training on the grounds of sexual orientation and religion and by December 2006 by age.

What can you do actively as a manager to encourage diversity and equal opportunity in the following areas:

Gender

Sexuality

Religion/belief

Disability

Childcare

Age

And generally to promote diversity at work?

Suggested answers

Gender

- Encourage both women and men to take development seriously
- Consider both women and men on their merits. Don't overlook women for promotion, deputising, temporary positions on the grounds of domestic responsibility or working patterns

Sexuality

- Ensure a working environment in which everyone feels respected and valued for what they do and the contribution they make
- Do not make judgements based on what people look like, what their background is or how they choose to live their lives

Religion/belief

- Consider religious beliefs when arranging meetings and training events, e.g. consider fasting times, different learning styles
- Take into account different dietary requirements
- Understand that some staff may celebrate religious observances and festivals
- Be aware of cultural differences when meeting or interviewing others, e.g. some people may avoid making eye contact

Disability

- Provide appropriate disability awareness for the team and for yourself
- Foster an atmosphere that encourages disclosure of a disability
- Make adjustments to the workplace as required

Childcare

- Offer childcare facilities
- Offer flexible working hours to accommodate working parents

Age

- Don't make assumptions about staff's abilities on the grounds of age
- Do not think that an older person does not need or want to be developed
- Ensure there are no age limitations in recruitment

And generally to promote diversity at work?

- Review recruitment, appraisal, development and promotion processes at work
- Ensure bullying and harassment are dealt with effectively
- Consult and listen to staff
- Monitor the organisation's approach to diversity

Recommended reading

Trompenaars, Fons and Turner, Charles Hampden (2002) *Riding the Waves of Culture: Understanding Cultural Diversity in Business*, Nicholas Brealey Publishing, London.

13
Emotional intelligence

Use this quiz to help people understand and recognise the elements that make up emotional intelligence.

Emotional intelligence

Emotional intelligence is defined by Daniel Goleman author of *Working with Emotional Intelligence* (Bloomsbury, London, 1999) as 'the capacity for recognising our feelings and those of others, for motivating ourselves and for managing emotions well in ourselves and in our relationships'.

There are four aspects of EQ:

- Self-awareness
- Self-management
- Awareness of others
- Relating to others

Answer the questions which relate to each of these four areas to better understand the nature of emotional intelligence.

Self-awareness

1 Which of the following characterise emotional self-awareness:

   a) I know what motivates me
   b) I know when I am angry, sad, happy, frightened
   c) Occasionally I am not aware of the impact my behaviour has on others
   d) I know what skills I am competent in
   e) I am aware of situations that cause me to think negatively
   f) I am confident in myself
   g) Sometimes I do not know why I act like I do

Self-management

2 Which of the following do NOT characterise emotional self-management:

   a) My anger tends to be explosive
   b) I take set-backs in my stride
   c) If something goes wrong at the start of the day, I know the rest of the day will be bad too
   d) I set myself achievable goals
   e) I am adaptable
   f) I sometimes lack initiative and drive
   g) I use positive 'self-talk' to help me achieve my goals

Awareness of others

3 Which of the following behaviours characterise emotional awareness of others:

   a) I recognise others when they have done a good job
   b) I am sensitive to my team members' needs
   c) I know when someone says something that they do not really mean

d) I sense when others are not happy

e) I do not know what makes my team tick

f) I know when to contribute to a conversation and when to stay silent

g) I know what is important to the people with whom I work

Relating to others

4 Which of the following do NOT characterise emotional intelligence in relating to others:

a) I can chat with some people in the team on a friendly basis

b) I find it easy to develop others' potential

c) Helping others through change is not always easy

d) I find it difficult sometimes to influence others to my way of thinking

e) I build trust with my customers and my team

f) If someone is having a hard time, I am supportive to them

g) Sometimes I find it easier to deal with facts than feelings

Suggested answers

Self-awareness

1 The following characterise emotional self-awareness:

    a) I know what motivates me
    b) I know when I am angry, sad, happy, frightened
    e) I am aware of situations that cause me to think negatively
    f) I am confident in myself

Self-management

2 The following do NOT characterise emotional self-management:

    a) My anger tends to be explosive
    c) If something goes wrong at the start of the day, I know the rest of the day will be bad too
    f) I sometimes lack initiative and drive

Awareness of others

3 The following behaviours characterise emotional awareness of others:

    a) I recognise others when they have done a good job
    b) I am sensitive to my team members' needs
    c) I know when someone says something that they do not really mean
    d) I sense when others are not happy
    f) I know when to contribute to a conversation and when to stay silent

Relating to others

4 The following do NOT characterise emotional intelligence relating to others:

    a) I can chat with some people in the team on a friendly basis
    c) Helping others through change is not always easy
    d) I find it difficult sometimes to influence others to my way of thinking
    g) Sometimes I find it easier to deal with facts than feelings

Recommended reading

Coleman, Daniel (1999) *Working with Emotional Intelligence*, Bloomsbury, London.
Ash, Eve and Quarry, Peter (2003) *The Emotional Competences Indicator*, Gower Publishing, Aldershot.

14
Empowerment

This quiz is designed to help individuals assess what empowerment is and their approach to the topic.

Empowerment

Answer the following questions:

1 What does the word empowerment mean to you?

2 What are three benefits of empowerment?

3 In what kind of environments/situations may empowerment not work?

4 What three key things does a manager need to do to empower his or her team?

5 What three things does an empowered employee need to do to ensure they are empowered?

6 Why do staff sometimes not accept empowerment?

Suggested answers

1 What does the word empowerment mean to you?

Empowerment is the devolvement of decision making to the lowest level

2 What are three benefits of empowerment?

Benefits of empowerment include:

- greater decision making for individuals
- more sense of ownership
- higher levels of customer satisfaction as staff have the power to make decisions to increase customer loyalty

3 In what kind of environments/situations may empowerment not work?

- highly regulatory environments
- crisis situations where clear command and control is needed

4 What three key things does a manager need to do to empower his or her team?

- communicate the benefits of empowerment
- set guidelines for empowerment and provide training in these
- provide appropriate motivational and developmental feedback

5 What three things does an empowered employee need to do to ensure they are empowered?

- understand the guidelines for empowerment
- ask for training and development in areas where they are not competent or confident
- provide feedback to their line manager on issues or concerns

6 Why do staff sometimes not accept empowerment?

- the benefits have not been communicated to them properly
- they do not want to take on perceived additional responsibility
- their manager has not provided clear guidelines, training or support

Recommended reading

Byham, William C. and Cox, Jeff (1999) *Zapp!: the Lightning of Empowerment*, Century, London.

15
Facilitation skills

This quiz will help individuals identify the key skills of facilitation.

Facilitation skills

Read the following situation and identify the key facilitation skills as demonstrated by Ruth:

Ruth is an external facilitator. She has been asked by a client to facilitate a meeting of a senior management team. This is the second meeting that Ruth has facilitated for this group. The objective of the meeting is for the group to agree a strategy for the organisation going forward.

Ruth arrives early at the venue and sets up the room. She has already had a discussion with the meeting sponsor before the event to better understand the desired outcomes. She greets the members of senior management as they arrive and makes them feel at ease.

To begin the meeting Ruth explains her role and asks the group, since this is the second meeting they have held on the topic, to agree some ground rules for working together to make the day as effective as possible.

Ruth introduces the first agenda topic. A debate ensues, during which Ruth notices that the three stronger characters dominate the air time. Ruth asks for a volunteer from the group to summarise the opinions stated so far. She then asks: 'What other views are there in the group?' One other member of the group voices an opinion but their point is strongly opposed by one of the stronger characters in the group.

Ruth refers the group to the ground rules that they have established and makes an observation about the uneven distribution of contribution so far. Several of the quieter members of the group then state their views. The first topic on the agenda is concluded.

In order to encourage greater debate around the second item on the agenda, Ruth suggests that the group divides into pairs and discusses the topic prior to sharing their thoughts with the rest of the group. This seems to encourage greater dialogue. However, when the second of the pairs feeds back their comments to the rest of the group, another member of the group talks over them. This person also does not allow another pair to finish their feedback. Ruth makes an observation on this behaviour and asks the group how they want to proceed. The group agrees that they should respect each other's views more and listen to what others have to say.

Ruth senses that the energy levels are low in the group at this point. She makes this observation and asks the group whether they want to take a break.

After 15 minutes' break the meeting reconvenes. Ruth notices that in discussing the third and final topic on the agenda, the debate is much more even and considered. At the end of the discussion the group reaches agreement about the strategy for the organisation going forward.

Suggested answers

The facilitator is a neutral servant of the group. His or her role is to encourage participation and help the group meet its objectives. Ruth's skills of facilitation are:

Preparation: Ruth arrives early at the venue and sets up the room. She has already had a discussion with the meeting sponsor before the event to better understand the desired outcomes.

Rapport building: She greets the members of senior management as they arrive and makes them feel at ease.

Establishing ground rules: To begin the meeting Ruth explains her role and asks the group, since this is the second meeting they have held on the topic, to agree some ground rules for working together to make the day as effective as possible.

Listening and observation skills: Ruth introduces the first agenda topic. A debate ensues, during which Ruth notices that the three stronger characters dominate the air time.

Intervention skills: Ruth asks for a volunteer from the group to summarise the opinions stated so far.

Questioning skills: She then asks: 'What other views are there in the group?' One other member of the group voices an opinion but their point is strongly opposed by one of the stronger characters in the group.

Neutrality and intervention skills to keep the group on track: Ruth refers the group to the ground rules that they have established and makes an observation about the uneven distribution of contribution so far. Several of the quieter members of the group then state their views. The first topic on the agenda is concluded.

Intervention skills: In order to encourage greater debate around the second item on the agenda, Ruth suggests that the group divides into pairs and discusses the topic prior to sharing their thoughts with the rest of the group. This seems to encourage greater dialogue.

Listening, observation, intervention, feedback and questioning skills:
However, when the second of the pairs feeds back their comments to the rest of the group, another member of the group talks over them. This person also does not allow another pair to finish their feedback. Ruth makes an observation on this behaviour and asks the group how they want to proceed. The group agrees that they should respect each other's views more and listen to what others have to say.

Observation, intervention and questioning skills: Ruth senses that the energy levels are low in the group at this point. She makes this observation and asks the group whether they want to take a break.

Observation skills: After 15 minutes' break the meeting reconvenes. Ruth notices that in discussing the third and final topic on the agenda, the debate is much more even and considered. At the end of the discussion the group reaches agreement about the strategy for the organisation going forward.

Recommended reading

Bee, Frances and Bee, Roland (1998) *Facilitation Skills Training Essentials*, Chartered Institute of Personnel Development, Wimbledon.
Hunter, Dale, Bailey, Anne and Taylor, Bill (1998) *The Facilitation of Groups*, Gower Publishing, Aldershot.

16
Feedback skills

This questionnaire is designed to assess individuals' beliefs about and approach to feedback. The responses to each question can be used as the basis for discussion. Ideal answers are included at the end.

Feedback skills

1 What is the purpose of feedback?

2 When is the most appropriate time to give feedback?

3 What are the common reasons people don't give feedback?

4 What is the effect on the individual of receiving positive, motivational feedback if done in an appropriate manner?

5 What is the effect on the individual of giving developmental, formative feedback if done in an appropriate manner?

6 What is the best way to give feedback?

7 What is the effect on the individual of sandwiching developmental feedback between positive feedback? For example, 'Your presentation was very good. You spoke very softly during the middle part, but overall it contained useful information.'

8 Why should you not give feedback on someone's personality?

9 What typically are the reactions you have experienced from others when giving them feedback?

10 How do you deal with someone who argues with you when receiving feedback?

Suggested answers

1 What is the purpose of feedback?

Feedback is communication to a person which gives them information about their performance, their behaviour and its impact on others

2 When is the most appropriate time to give feedback?

Feedback is best given at or as near as possible to the event. People should not wait for annual performance reviews to give feedback. It should be an ongoing everyday activity

3 What are the common reasons people don't give feedback?

Some people hold back from giving motivational feedback because:

- They feel too embarrassed
- They believe that the person receiving the feedback may be suspicious of their motives
- They think that compliments are inappropriate, because the staff member is only doing what they are paid to do

Some people hold back from giving formative/developmental feedback because:

- They worry that they might upset the receiver
- They are concerned that the receiver may reject them/reject the feedback
- They are concerned that it may end in a confrontation that would be difficult to resolve and might damage future relations

4 What is the effect on the individual of receiving positive, motivational feedback if done in an appropriate manner?

Giving motivational feedback builds people's confidence by encouraging them to do more of the same

5 What is the effect on the individual of giving developmental, formative feedback if done in an appropriate manner?

Giving developmental feedback builds people's competence by indicating to them what they need to do differently

6 What is the best way to give feedback?

- Start with the motivational because it encourages the person to listen
- Follow with developmental feedback, what can be improved
- Ask the staff member what they thought about their performance
- Offer specific examples of the observed performance/behaviour

- Describe behaviour and its *effect* on you/others
- Ask the person how they might vary or do things differently
- Listen to what the person has to say before you comment
- Offer alternatives/suggestions where improvement is needed

7 What is the effect on the individual of sandwiching developmental feedback between positive, motivational feedback? For example, 'Your presentation was very good. You spoke too softly during the middle part, but overall it contained useful information'

The effect is that the developmental feedback gets lost between the two pieces of motivational feedback. The receiver will not be clear what it is that you would like them to change. Likewise, linking motivational and developmental feedback with 'but' or 'however' kills the motivational feedback; for example, 'your presentation was very well structured but you spoke too softly during the middle part'

8 Why should you not give feedback on someone's personality?

Feedback should refer to relevant performance/behaviour, not personality. It should focus on behaviours that can be changed. If you offer perceptions and opinions state them as that, not as fact

9 What typically are the reactions you have experienced from others when giving them feedback?

Typical reactions to feedback can include:

DENIAL –	not ME!
EMOTION –	how can you do this to me?
RATIONALISATION –	ah, may be, BUT . . .
ACCEPTANCE –	well, yes, it's true
CHANGE –	I know what I am going to do

We all tend to go through these stages when receiving feedback

10 How do you deal with someone who argues with you when receiving feedback?

Stay calm. Provide evidence of their behaviour. Listen to what they have to say. If the behaviour persists, ask to postpone the discussion until later. Make sure, however, that you do continue the discussion at a later date

Recommended reading

Bishop, Sue (2000) *The Complete Feedback Skills Training Book*, Gower Publishing, Aldershot.

17
Handling difficult customer situations

This quiz will help customer service front-line staff consider how to deal with difficult customer situations.

Handling difficult customer situations

Look at the following customer situations and write down what you would say in reply:

1 A customer approaches you and says they have been waiting over six weeks for a query to be resolved.

What do you say?

2 A customer telephones you and is very agitated that no one has called them back to let them know what is happening about their complaint. They spoke to someone in your office over two weeks ago and it seems that the message has not been passed to this office.

What do you say?

3 A customer contacts you and is very agitated because the product he has bought is faulty. It is only one month old.

What do you say?

4 The daughter of an elderly customer calls. Her father is very ill and can no longer deal with his own affairs. She wants to know who to contact in your organisation about his account. She has already sent in a letter to ask about this but has still not had a reply.

What do you say?

5 A customer comes in to see you. She has called the company and been passed around six times from one part of the organisation without anyone resolving her query. She is very angry and has decided to come in to see you in person.

What do you say?

6 A customer calls and complains that she has been waiting over a month for a reply to her letter. She explains that she has had this problem once before and it took over three months to sort out. She really thinks that it's inefficient, particularly given all the problems she's had before.

What do you say?

Suggested response

In handling difficult customer situations it is very important to acknowledge what the customer is feeling, before dealing with the facts of the situation.

Often when customers are being 'difficult' their emotions are running high. They cannot deal rationally with the issue or complaint until they believe that you understand their situation. Customers will not listen to you unless you show that you have really listened to them.

The first steps in dealing with a difficult customer situation therefore should be to:

- Listen actively: Allow the customer to let off steam. Make listening noises but do not interrupt
- Apologise if at fault: If you are wrong, say so. A sincere apology if you are at fault will often diffuse a situation
- Show empathy and understanding of the situation: Put yourself in the customer's shoes. Use phrases such as 'I appreciate ...'; 'I understand ...'; 'I'm sorry to hear ...'. Importantly, make sure that what you say sounds sincere
- Show a willingness to help: Use phrases such as 'I will certainly do my best to help you'
- Only then, once you have acknowledged the customer's feelings, should you question the customer, start dealing with the facts of the complaint, take ownership of the problem and go on to resolve it.

Look back at your responses to the questions.

If you have not acknowledged the customer's feelings **before** you dealt with the facts of the situation, revisit your answers.

Recommended reading

Rourke, Dennis (2003) *Managing Your Most Difficult Customers*, Homebuilder Pr, New York.

18
Health and safety

Use this quiz to assess individuals' knowledge of the health and safety procedures in your organisation.

Health and safety

Staying safe at work is important to all of us. Take a few minutes to answer the following questions:

1 What is the name of the Health and Safety Co-ordinator in your area?
2 What is/are the name(s) of the qualified first aider(s) in your area?
3 What are the locations of the first aid boxes?
4 What are the procedures for reporting accidents?
5 What action do you take if the fire alarm rings?
6 Where are the assembly points?
7 What do you do if you discover a fire?

8 Where are the fire alarms?
9 How do you escape from the building?
10 What special arrangements are there for colleagues with disabilities?
11 Where is the fire-fighting equipment located?
12 What types of fire extinguishers are there?
13 Do you know how to use them?

Recommended reading

Ridley, John (2001) *Health & Safety in Brief*, Butterworth-Heinemann, London.

19
Induction

Use this quiz to help people consolidate what they have learned during induction.

Induction: 20 questions

Answer the following questions:

  1 When was the organisation established?

  2 What is the organisation's vision/mission?

  3 What are the organisation's values?

  4 Who heads the organisation?

  5 What is the name of your head of department?

  6 In which locations is the organisation based?

  7 Who are the organisation's key customers?

  8 What are the key products and services we sell?

  9 Who are your external customers?

10 Who are your internal customers?

11 What is the standard greeting on the telephone?

12 What is your email address?

13 Where are the fire exits in your area?

14 Where is the fire assembly point?

15 Who are the first aid officers in your area?

16 What are your working hours?

17 What are the arrangements for lunch and breaks?

18 What is your holiday entitlement?

19 Who do you contact if you have a query about payroll?

20 What are the areas in which you would like more information to help you in your new job?

20
Influencing skills

By using this quiz participants will be able to distinguish between 'push' behaviours which encourage other people to do things differently, and 'pull' behaviours which signal that you are willing to change. A combination of both approaches is the key to effective influencing.

Influencing skills

In order to influence effectively, managers need to use a balance of 'push' and 'pull' techniques. Using the model below as reference, identify whether the statements that follow are examples of 'push' or 'pull' techniques.

Influencing skills summary

Push	Pull
Stating views and opinions	Actively listening
Stating what I want	Questioning
Stating incentives and consequences	Building on common ground
Disclosing feelings	Being open
IMPACT: SIGNALS YOU WANT THE OTHER PERSON TO CHANGE	IMPACT: SIGNALS YOU ARE PREPARED TO LEARN MORE AND POSSIBLY CHANGE

Statement	Push or pull behaviour
'In my opinion we need to …'	
'So what you're saying is'	
'I need to know when you need it by'	
'How did this happen?'	
'You're right, we did make an error there'	
'If you do that, I'd be prepared to …'	
'I agree, that's a good idea'	
'I believe that's the best way because …'	
'So, we all agree that we should …'	
'You don't sound as though you are convinced'	
'What do you think we should do next?'	
'I want you to be responsible for timekeeping'	
'Right now I'm feeling as though we're not getting anywhere'	
'I feel really pleased about what we have achieved so far'	
'I am quite good at this type of activity'	
'I suggest we do this first'	
'If you do that we will run out of time'	

Suggested answers

Statement	Push or pull behaviour
'In my opinion we need to ...'	Push – stating views and opinions
'So what you're saying is'	Pull – active listening
'I need to know when you need it by'	Push – stating what I want
'How did this happen?'	Pull – questioning
'You're right, we did make an error there'	Pull – being open
'If you do that, I'd be prepared to ...'	Push – stating incentives and consequences
'I agree, that's a good idea'	Pull – building common ground
'I believe that's the best way because ...'	Push – stating views and opinions
'So, we all agree that we should ...'	Pull – building common ground
'You don't sound as though you are convinced'	Pull – active listening
'What do you think we should do next?'	Pull – questioning
'I want you to be responsible for timekeeping'	Push – stating what I want
'Right now I'm feeling as though we're not getting anywhere'	Push – disclosing feelings
'I feel really pleased about what we have achieved so far'	Push – disclosing feelings
'I am quite good at this type of activity'	Pull – being open
'I suggest we do this first'	Push – stating views and opinions
'If you do that we will run out of time'	Push – stating incentives and consequences

Recommended reading

Laborde, Genie Z. (1984) *Influencing with Integrity: Management Skills for Communication and Negotiation*, Crown House Publishing, New York.

21
Interviewing poor performers

This quiz is designed to allow individuals to better understand the best approach to interviewing poor performers.

Interviewing poor performers

Imagine that you need to hold a discussion with one of your team who has arrived half an hour late three days out of five each week during the last month.

Which of the following statements is it most appropriate to use?

At the beginning of the interview

A How are things going? Have you any problems at home?

B I want to speak to you about your timekeeping. I've noticed that you have arrived half an hour late three days out of five for the past month. Can you explain why this is?

C You've arrived late three days out of five for the past month and this is not acceptable. Your contract states that you will arrive by 9 a.m. each day.

D Do you realise that you're letting the team down each time you arrive late?

During the interview

A The situation must change. It is not fair on the rest of us for you not to be here to answer the phone first thing in the morning

B We do need to resolve this situation. The impact of you not being here for the first half hour of the day is that our level of customer service drops as the phones are not answered quickly. What suggestions do you have to ensure you do arrive on time?

C You need to get an earlier bus if the one you normally get is unreliable

D I can appreciate that buses are running late in the mornings because of congestion. Would you like to alter your hours so that you come in later?

At the end of the interview

A So we've agreed that you'll ensure you get an earlier bus

B So we're both clear, please tell me what we've agreed and when we'll review this

C In spite of your poor timekeeping, you are making a significant contribution to the team

D We'll talk about this again next week. If this is not resolved by then I'm afraid we'll have to instigate the disciplinary procedure

Suggested answers

At the beginning of the interview

B I want to speak to you about your timekeeping. I've noticed that you have arrived half an hour late three days out of five for the past month. Can you explain why this is?

It is important at the beginning of the interview to:

- Explain the purpose of the discussion
- Provide evidence of the poor performance
- Ask the interviewee the reasons for their poor performance and listen to their response

During the interview

B We do need to resolve this situation. The impact of you not being here for the first half hour of the day is that our level of customer service drops as the phones are not answered quickly. What suggestions do you have to ensure you do arrive on time?

During the interview the interviewer needs to:

- Explain that the situation must change
- Point out the impact of the poor performance
- Ask the interviewee for their ideas on how to resolve the situation
- Listen and build on their ideas, don't try to impose their own solutions

At the end of the interview

B So we're both clear, please tell me what we've agreed and when we'll review this

At the end of the interview the interviewee needs to:

- Agree a plan of action and when this will be reviewed
- Ask the interviewee to summarise the plan of action and the review time in order to check their understanding

Recommended reading

Cooper, Maureen and Curtis, Bev (2000) *Managing Poor Performance*, Network Educational Press Ltd, London.

22
Leadership styles

Use this quiz to help people identify different leadership styles. You may also invite a discussion on the impact of each style.

Leadership styles

In each of the following statements there are four different leadership styles.
Identify the four styles:

1
   a) I tend to leave my team to their own devices
   b) I seek to maintain a steady pace of work with my team
   c) I drive my team hard to achieve their goals
   d) I am supportive to my team

2
   a) I avoid conflict at all cost
   b) I try to avoid conflict but if it occurs I try to smooth things over in a friendly way
   c) When there is conflict I defend my position with counter-arguments
   d) When there is conflict I keep calm and try to develop a joint solution

3
   a) My style is collegiate
   b) My style is defensive
   c) My style is laissez-faire
   d) My style is consultative

4
   a) I rarely give feedback on others' performance
   b) I find it easy to give motivational feedback
   c) I tell people how they can improve
   d) My feedback is a balance of motivational and developmental advice

5
   a) I place high value on maintaining good relations
   b) I tend to do my own thing
   c) I search for workable solutions
   d) I tend to impose my decisions

6
   a) I use my humour to maintain friendly situations or when there is disagreement,
      to shift away from serious discussion
   b) My humour can be seen by others as rather pointless
   c) My humour is hard hitting
   d) My humour fits the situation and I retain a sense of humour even under
      pressure

Suggested answers

The four leadership styles are:

HIGH	High support Low challenge **COUNSELLOR**	High support High challenge **COACH**
Support	Low support Low challenge **ABDICATOR**	Low support High challenge **TASK MASTER**
LOW	LOW	HIGH

Challenge

1

    a) I tend to leave my team to their own devices – **Abdicator**

    b) I seek to maintain a steady pace of work with my team – **Coach**

    c) I drive my team hard to achieve their goals – **Taskmaster**

    d) I am supportive to my team – **Counsellor**

2

    a) I avoid conflict at all cost – **Abdicator**

    b) I try to avoid conflict but if it occurs I try to smooth things over in a friendly way – **Counsellor**

    c) When there is conflict I defend my position with counter-arguments – **Taskmaster**

    d) When there is conflict I keep calm and try to develop a joint solution – **Coach**

3

    a) My style is collegiate – **Counsellor**

    b) My style can be seen as aggressive – **Taskmaster**

    c) My style is laissez-faire – **Abdicator**

    d) My style is consultative – **Coach**

4

    a) I rarely give feedback on others' performance – **Abdicator**

    b) I find it easy to give motivational feedback – **Counsellor**

    c) I tell people what they need to do differently – **Taskmaster**

    d) My feedback is a balance of motivational and developmental advice – **Coach**

5

    a) I place high value on maintaining good relations – **Counsellor**

    b) I tend to do my own thing – **Abdicator**

    c) I search for workable solutions – **Coach**

    d) I tend to impose my decisions – **Taskmaster**

6

    a) I use my humour to maintain friendly situations or when there is disagreement, to shift away from serious discussion – **Counsellor**

    b) My humour can be seen by others as rather pointless – **Abdicator**

    c) My humour is hard hitting – **Taskmaster**

    d) My humour fits the situation and I retain a sense of humour even under pressure – **Coach**

Recommended reading

Beck, John D. W. and Yeager, Neil M. (2001) *The Leader's Window: Mastering the Four Styles of Leadership to Build High-Performing Teams*, Davies-Black Publishing, New York.

23
Learning styles

This quiz tests people's understanding of learning styles.

Learning styles

Research shows that there are four learning styles. Those of:

- The Doer
- The Thinker
- The Practical and
- The Rationalist

Listed below are characteristics of the learning styles of each of these four types. Select which behaviour belongs to which style.

Behaviour	Learning style
1 Integrate their observations into logical theory	
2 Involve themselves in new experiences	
3 Stand back and observe	
4 Keen to try out new idea	
5 Think problems through in a logical way	
6 Assimilate disparate information into logical theories	
7 Live in the 'here and now'	
8 Find better ways of doing things	
9 Listen and then speak	
10 Use brainstorming to overcome problems	
11 Want to see ideas and theories work in practice	
12 Are perfectionists	
13 Prefer to reflect on things before coming to a conclusion	
14 Search out new ideas and apply them	
15 Collect and thoroughly analyse experiences	
16 Worry unless things fit into a logical scheme	
17 Enthusiastic about new things	
18 Tend to postpone reaching conclusions	
19 Want to try things out in practice	
20 Appear slightly distant	
21 Like to analyse	
22 Down to earth	

23 Get bored easily	
24 Take a back seat in meetings and discussions	
25 Look for new challenges	
26 Keen on making sure things make sense	
27 Open-minded	
28 Enjoy observation	
29 Like to get on with things	
30 Like theories, models and concepts	
31 Act first, think second	
32 Act quickly to turn new ideas into practice	
33 Get impatient with lengthy discussions	
34 Seek to be the centre of activity	
35 Prefer information to have a practical application	
36 Like solving problems	
37 Detached and analytical	
38 Consider all angles	
39 Will try anything once	
40 Are good listeners	
41 Logical	
42 Cautious	
43 Gregarious	
44 Dislike subjectivity and flippancy	

Suggested answers

Behaviour	Learning style
1 Integrate their observations into logical theory	The Rationalist
2 Involve themselves in new experiences	The Doer
3 Stand back and observe	The Thinker
4 Keen to try out new idea	The Practical
5 Think problems through in a logical way	The Rationalist
6 Assimilate disparate information into logical theories	The Rationalist
7 Live in the 'here and now'	The Doer
8 Find better ways of doing things	The Practical
9 Listen and then speak	The Thinker
10 Use brainstorming to overcome problems	The Doer
11 Want to see ideas and theories work in practice	The Practical
12 Are perfectionists	The Rationalist
13 Prefer to reflect on things before coming to a conclusion	The Thinker
14 Search out new ideas and apply them	The Practical
15 Collect and thoroughly analyse experiences	The Thinker
16 Worry unless things fit into a logical scheme	The Rationalist
17 Enthusiastic about new things	The Doer
18 Tend to postpone reaching conclusions	The Thinker
19 Want to try things out in practice	The Practical
20 Appear slightly distant	The Thinker
21 Like to analyse	The Rationalist
22 Down to earth	The Practical
23 Get bored easily	The Doer
24 Take a back seat in meetings and discussions	The Thinker
25 Look for new challenges	The Doer
26 Keen on making sure things make sense	The Rationalist
27 Open-minded	The Doer
28 Enjoy observation	The Thinker
29 Like to get on with things	The Practical

COMPENDIUM OF LEARNING AND DEVELOPMENT QUIZZES

30 Like theories, models and concepts	The Rationalist
31 Act first, think second	The Doer
32 Act quickly to turn new ideas into practice	The Practical
33 Get impatient with lengthy discussions	The Practical
34 Seek to be the centre of activity	The Doer
35 Prefer information to have a practical application	The Practical
36 Like solving problems	The Practical
37 Detached and analytical	The Rationalist
38 Consider all angles	The Thinker
39 Will try anything once	The Doer
40 Are good listeners	The Thinker
41 Logical	The Rationalist
42 Cautious	The Thinker
43 Gregarious	The Doer
44 Dislike subjectivity and flippancy	The Rationalist

Recommended reading

Honey, Peter and Mumford, Alan (2000) *The Learning Styles Helper's Guide*, Peter Honey Publications, Maidenhead.

24
Listening skills

This quiz helps individuals assess what are good and bad listening skills.

Listening skills

Below is a list of attributes of good and bad listeners. Consider each statement in turn and decide whether they are good or bad:

1 Listen to content   Good ☐   Bad ☐

2 Try to really understand, getting the full meaning   Good ☐   Bad ☐

3 Spend time when listening getting ready to talk   Good ☐   Bad ☐

4 Allow themselves to daydream   Good ☐   Bad ☐

5 Do one thing at a time – listen   Good ☐   Bad ☐

6 Ask for confirmation if required   Good ☐   Bad ☐

7 Question when necessary   Good ☐   Bad ☐

8 Use silence to show they are listening   Good ☐   Bad ☐

9 Listen for main ideas   Good ☐   Bad ☐

10 Control their emotions   Good ☐   Bad ☐

11 Listen for facts, themes and impressions   Good ☐   Bad ☐

12 Concentrate, fighting distractions   Good ☐   Bad ☐

13 Divide their attention or try to do something else   Good ☐   Bad ☐

14 Pay particular attention to emotional words   Good ☐   Bad ☐

15 Keep an open mind   Good ☐   Bad ☐

16 Want people to 'get on with it'   Good ☐   Bad ☐

17 Check understanding   Good ☐   Bad ☐

18 Take a part meaning from the conversation   Good ☐   Bad ☐

19 Maintain patience and concentration   Good ☐   Bad ☐

20 Nod and make eye contact   Good ☐   Bad ☐

21 Summarise key points using the speaker's language   Good ☐   Bad ☐

22 Summarise key points in their own words   Good ☐   Bad ☐

23 Use unresponsive body language   Good ☐   Bad ☐

24 Listen to style, for example grammar   Good ☐   Bad ☐

Suggested answers

Good listeners

1 Listen to content

2 Try to really understand, getting the full meaning

5 Do one thing at a time – listen

6 Ask for confirmation if required

7 Question when necessary

10 Control their emotions

11 Listen for facts, themes and impressions

12 Concentrate, fighting distractions

15 Keep an open mind

17 Check understanding

19 Maintain patience and concentration

20 Nod and make eye contact

22 Summarise key points using the speaker's language

Bad listeners

3 Spend time when listening getting ready to talk

4 Allow themselves to daydream

8 Use silence to show they are listening

9 Listen for main ideas

13 Divide their attention or try to do something else

14 Pay particular attention to emotional words

16 Want people to 'get on with it'

18 Take a part meaning from the conversation

22 Summarise key points in their own words

23 Use unresponsive body language

24 Listen to style, for example grammar

Recommended reading

Mackay, Ian (1998) *Listening Skills (Management Shapers)*, Chartered Institute of Personnel & Development, Wimbledon.

25
Managing change

This quiz helps individuals recognise their own and others' reactions to change. In doing this it will help them identify ways in which to effectively manage change.

Managing change

There are seven phases that people go through when faced with organisational change. The time spent in each phase is dependent upon the individual and how well people are encouraged to express their emotions during change.

1 Shock A sense of being overwhelmed. Reality doesn't meet expectations.

2 Denial Building up your defences and minimising the disruption. Behaviour based on the past rather than the present.

3 Self-doubt Reality of change becoming apparent and causing uncertainty. A feeling of sinking rather than swimming.

4 Acceptance Unhooking from the past and letting go. A willingness to experiment with change. Optimism for the future becomes possible.

5 Testing Trying out new behaviours to cope with the transition. Lots of activity and energy; mistakes liable.

6 Internalising Searching for the meaning of how and why there was a change; withdrawal from activity and sharing of insights. A quiet, reflective period.

7 Integration Incorporating meanings into new behaviours. Stable conditions. The final stage of transition is now over. New and better ways developed. Increased self-esteem.

Quiz on managing change

Given the phases of change, identify which of the following behaviours and thoughts belong to which phase:

What am I doing here?	_____
Maybe there's a role for me in the future	_____
I can't sleep at night	_____
Productivity increases in the short term	_____
Over-preparation	_____
On reflection I can see why change was needed	_____
It will soon be over	_____
Anger/fights	_____
It might not be as bad as I thought	_____
Apathy	_____
Numbness	_____
I feel more able to cope	_____
Frustration at getting things wrong	_____
I found it difficult to change because . . .	_____
I feel confident and competent	_____
We have to move on	_____
Team work is very good	_____
It probably won't happen anyway	_____
I gave my all and now look what I get	_____
I have too many ideas	_____
Satisfaction	_____
I can see where I was going wrong	_____
I'll keep my head down and hopefully it will go away	_____
We have a clear focus and plan	_____
In the past we did it . . .	_____
I'm not sure what to do	_____
I have too much to do	_____
On reflection it was for the best	_____

Suggested answers

What am I doing here?	Shock
Maybe there's a role for me in the future	Acceptance
I can't sleep at night	Self-doubt
Productivity increases in the short term	Denial
Over-preparation	Testing
On reflection I can see why change was needed	Internalising
It will soon be over	Shock
Anger/fights	Self-doubt
It might not be as bad as I thought	Acceptance
Apathy	Shock
Numbness	Shock
I feel more able to cope	Acceptance
Frustration at getting things wrong	Testing
I found it difficult to change because ...	Internalising
I feel confident and competent	Integration
We have to move on	Acceptance
Team work is very good	Integration
It probably won't happen anyway	Denial
I gave my all and now look what I get	Self-doubt
I have too many ideas	Testing
Satisfaction	Integration
I can see where I was going wrong	Internalising
I'll keep my head down and hopefully it will go away	Denial
We have a clear focus and plan	Integration
In the past we did it ...	Denial
I'm not sure what to do	Self-doubt
I have too much to do	Testing
I can understand now why I found it difficult	Internalising

Recommended reading

Burnes, Bernard (2000) *Managing Change*, Prentice Hall, London.

26
Meeting skills

This is a fun quiz that summarises the key skills of the meeting leader.

Meeting skills

Find the statements and words that describe the skills and actions that an effective meeting leader will take:

S	T	I	N	V	O	L	V	E	E	V	E	R	Y	O	N	E	N	Q
C	T	O	S	P	K	A	S	D	F	G	H	J	K	L	Z	X	O	U
A	L	A	X	E	C	E	V	B	N	M	K	O	P	E	F	O	I	E
R	P	E	R	Y	N	D	E	S	C	A	V	R	I	F	Q	X	U	S
L	Z	P	L	T	T	D	O	P	S	C	T	D	T	M	E	R	H	T
E	S	R	O	T	O	D	A	C	O	S	Z	G	M	N	S	A	L	I
T	N	S	C	I	D	N	S	G	L	N	G	H	A	O	J	P	O	O
U	Q	S	E	R	N	Y	T	W	E	U	T	I	L	I	S	T	E	N
E	A	R	U	T	H	T	Y	I	F	N	C	R	S	P	I	N	S	R
E	P	D	F	R	G	P	T	U	M	N	D	T	A	I	L	I	F	P
T	H	M	C	B	E	M	N	I	J	E	L	A	D	C	H	O	E	L
I	D	E	A	N	B	N	C	V	M	G	D	Y	B	A	K	J	R	O
X	X	V	O	L	V	E	O	T	H	E	S	H	C	E	F	T	T	I
D	D	A	D	F	G	E	T	T	R	F	K	U	V	S	F	F	P	U
S	S	U	M	M	A	R	I	S	E	R	A	E	T	G	C	O	W	Y
S	S	A	O	H	P	D	S	A	E	S	R	I	E	Y	S	E	R	W
Z	Z	W	K	J	W	E	Z	S	E	E	K	O	H	P	D	S	A	E
A	A	Q	L	E	U	F	R	D	R	T	F	E	J	W	E	Z	S	E
Q	Q	Z	K	L	N	H	X	X	F	A	S	L	P	U	F	R	D	R
T	T	R	T	Y	U	I	O	P	K	L	D	K	L	T	H	X	X	F

Answers

S		I	N	V	O	L	V	E	E	V	E	R	Y	O	N	E		Q
	T		S		K													U
A		A		E		E												E
	P		R		N		E											S
		P		T		D		P										T
E			O		O		A		O									I
	N			I		N		G		N								O
		S			N		T		E		T		L	I	S	T	E	N
			U			T		I		N		R						
				R			T		M		D		A					
					E			I		E		A		C				
						N			M				B		K			
							O			E				E				
								T			K				F			
	S	U	M	M	A	R	I	S	E			E				O		
										S			E				R	
											K			P				E
												E			E			
													P			R		
														T				

START ON TIME
INVOLVE EVERYONE
QUESTION
LISTEN
SUMMARISE
ENSURE NOTES KEPT
KEEP ON TRACK
SEND AGENDA BEFORE
APPOINT TIMEKEEPER

Recommended reading

Weiss, D. H. (1987) *How to Run a Meeting (Successful Office Skills SOS)*, Amacom, New York.

27
Mentoring skills

This quiz will help individuals identify the four stages of mentoring and the activities that take place in each one.

Mentoring skills

There are four phases of mentoring:

- Start up
- Direction setting
- Implementation
- Review

Below is a list of the activities that potentially could take place in each phase. Match the activity to the correct phase:

Activity	Start up	Direction setting	Implementation	Review
Discuss understanding of mentoring				
Diagnose the mentee's needs				
Progress the mentee's development areas				
Determine mentee's objectives				
Mentee puts plans into action				
Discuss mentee's key learning points				
Set up details of further meetings				
Agree how the mentor and mentee will work together				
Use the mentor's expertise				
Determine mentee's learning style and the implication of this for development				
Identify new issues and directions				
Identify priorities				

Activity	Start up	Direction setting	Implementation	Review
Think through how the mentor and the mentee's learning style may complement or hinder progress				
Mentor and mentee will decide whether they can work together				
Decide next steps				
Set measures of success				
Decide whether to maintain or end the relationship				
Review how mentor and mentee are working together				
Assess outputs against agreed success criteria				
Mentor reviews his/her own learning				

Suggested answers

Activity	Start up	Direction setting	Implementation	Review
Discuss understanding of mentoring	X			
Diagnose the mentee's needs		X		
Progress the mentee's development areas			X	
Determine mentee's objectives		X		
Mentee puts plans into action			X	
Discuss mentee's key learning points				X
Set up details of further meetings	X			
Agree how the mentor and mentee will work together	X			
Use the mentor's expertise			X	
Determine mentee's learning style and the implication of this for development		X		
Identify new issues and directions			X	
Identify priorities		X		
Think through how the mentor and the mentee's learning style may complement or hinder progress		X		
Mentor and mentee decide whether they can work together	X			
Decide next steps				X
Set measures of success		X		

Activity	Start up	Direction setting	Implementation	Review
Decide whether to maintain or end the relationship				X
Review how mentor and mentee are working together			X	
Assess outputs against agreed success criteria				X
Mentor reviews his/her own learning				X

Recommended reading

Clutterbuck, David (2001) *Everyone Needs a Mentor*, Chartered Institute of Personnel and Development, Wimbledon.

28
Motivating others

This quiz can be used to test an individual's attitude and approach to motivating others. It is based on the work of Herzberg and Spitzer.

Motivating others

Look at the following statements and decide whether each one is True or False. If you don't know the answer, tick Not sure.

1 You cannot motivate other people, you can only create the environment in which they want to give of their best: motivation comes from within

True ☐ False ☐ Not sure ☐

2 What motivates me will motivate the people on my team

True ☐ False ☐ Not sure ☐

3 Money is a long-term motivator

True ☐ False ☐ Not sure ☐

4 Having a pleasant environment in which to work is a motivator

True ☐ False ☐ Not sure ☐

5 Different things motivate different people

True ☐ False ☐ Not sure ☐

6 If you don't receive recognition for a job well done, you won't feel motivated

True ☐ False ☐ Not sure ☐

7 Giving people opportunities to advance is a means of motivation for some people

True ☐ False ☐ Not sure ☐

8 Setting people targets is a motivator

True ☐ False ☐ Not sure ☐

9 When people do not feel they are achieving anything, they become demotivated

True ☐ False ☐ Not sure ☐

10 Individuals can feel motivated, indifferent or demotivated at work

True ☐ False ☐ Not sure ☐

Suggested answers

1 You cannot motivate other people, you can only create the environment in which they want to give of their best: motivation comes from within: **True**. Motivation comes from within.

2 What motivates me will motivate the people on my team: **False**. Everyone has different motivators. It is a fallacy to expect what motivates you to motivate others.

3 Money is a long-term motivator: **False**. Money is important to people; however you can be in a highly paid job and still not be motivated. In Herzberg's terms money is a hygiene factor – if you are paid adequately you may not necessarily be motivated.

4 Having a pleasant environment in which to work is a motivator: **False**. In Herzberg's terms the working environment is a hygiene factor – if you work in a pleasant environment you may not necessarily be motivated.

5 Different things motivate different people: **True**. See Question 2.

6 If you don't receive recognition for a job well done, you won't feel motivated: **True and False**. Recognition is a motivator, but not for everybody.

7 Giving people opportunities to advance is a means of motivation for some people: **True**.

8 Setting people targets is a motivator: **False**. Setting targets is not a motivator in itself. For some people having targets which they then **achieve** can be a motivator.

9 When people do not feel they are achieving anything, they become demotivated: **True and False**. For some people achievement is a motivator.

10 Individuals can feel motivated, indifferent or demotivated at work: **True**.

Recommended reading

Spitzer, Dean (1995) *Super-motivation: A Blueprint for Energizing Your Organization from Top to Bottom*, Amacom, New York.

29
Negotiation skills

This quiz allows people to identify best practice in negotiation.

Negotiation skills

You are given two statements in answer to each question. Circle the letter which is most representative of the correct answer, where:

A and E are closest to the different statements
B and D less close
C is the middle between the two statements.

1 To what extent should you prepare before a negotiation?

To a great extent	A B C D E	To a little extent

2 To what extent should you consider the position and issues of the other party prior to the negotiation?

To a great extent	A B C D E	To a little extent

3 To what should you pay most attention when preparing for a negotiation?

The other party's strengths	A B C D E	The other party's weaknesses

4 What is the best way to regard the process of negotiating?

One party wins, the other loses	A B C D E	Both parties win

5 What should be the outcome of a negotiation?

A good result for your organisation	A B C D E	A good result for both parties

6 How often should you set clear objectives for a negotiation?

Always	A B C D E	Rarely

7 When negotiating should you hold fast to your objectives?

Always	A B C D E	Rarely

8 How often should you become impatient or lose your temper in a negotiation?

Always	A B C D E	Rarely

9 Which should you do more of in a negotiation?

Talk	A B C D E	Listen

10 What should you feel about making concessions in a negotiation?

Don't make concessions	A B C D E	Recognise the principles of giving and getting

11 How should you test assumptions in a negotiation?

Wait to hear what the other party has to say	A B C D E	Use open questions to test assumptions

12 If you have spent some time negotiating, but are not happy with the suggested outcome, how likely are you to reach agreement during the meeting?

Very unlikely	A B C D E	Very likely

13 As you work to reach agreement, who should normally sum up what has been agreed along the way?

You	A B C D E	The other party

14 What should you do when you are in a negotiation and you don't understand something?

Ask questions to clarify the matter	A B C D E	Let the matter pass without saying anything

15 What should you do when you are in a negotiation and the other party will not give anything away?

Feel that you've reached a stalemate and give up	A B C D E	Ask questions and explore possibilities

16 What should an effective negotiator's attitude be towards conflict in a negotiation?

Prefer to avoid conflict	A B C D E	Conflict is healthy and should be aired

17 How and when should you make concessions during a negotiation?

Make the concession early on in the negotiation	A B C D E	Make the concession slowly and make it look more significant than it is

18 When should you raise important issues during a negotiation?

Early on in the negotiation	A B C D E	Towards the end of the negotiation

19 With whom should you feel happier negotiating?

Someone on the same level as you	A B C D E	Anyone, irrespective of title or position

20 How often should you invent options/new ideas in negotiations?

Frequently	A B C D E	Rarely

Suggested answers

1 To what extent should you prepare before a negotiation?

To a great extent	**A** B C D E	To a little extent

2 To what extent should you consider the position and issues of the other party prior to the negotiation?

To a great extent	**A** B C D E	To a little extent

To a great extent – the best negotiators thoroughly assess the position of both parties before they begin negotiating.

3 To what should you pay most attention when preparing for a negotiation?

The other party's strengths	**A** B C D E	The other party's weaknesses

Effective negotiators pay particular attention to the other party's strengths and to their own weaknesses.

4 What is the best way to regard the process of negotiating?

One party wins, the other loses	A B C D **E**	**Both parties win**

5 What should be the outcome of a negotiation?

A good result for your organisation	A B C D **E**	**A good result for both parties**

A negotiation is not a competition, neither is it total co-operation. A negotiation has to be fair. If you try to make it competitive you will damage your relationship with the other party. A successful outcome will mean a win/win situation for both sides.

6 How often should you set clear objectives for a negotiation?

Always	**A** B C D E	Rarely

7 When negotiating should you hold fast to your objectives?

Always	A B **C** D E	Rarely

Effective negotiators always set objectives prior to the negotiation. They never lose sight of them during a negotiation. However, they are flexible in their approach and are prepared to produce new ideas.

8 How often should you become impatient or lose your temper in a negotiation?

Always	A B C D **E**	**Rarely**

Never lose your temper or become impatient in a negotiation. It gives advantage to the other side.

9 Which should you do more of in a negotiation?

Talk	A B C D **E**	**Listen**

You should listen more than talk in negotiations.

10 What should you feel about making concessions in a negotiation?

Don't make concessions	A B C D **E**	**Recognise the principles of giving and getting**

Making concessions helps both parties move towards agreement. Remember the principles of give and get.

11 How should you test assumptions in a negotiation?

Wait to hear what the other party has to say	A B C D **E**	**Use open questions to test assumptions**

Use open questions to test assumptions.

12 If you have spent some time negotiating, but are not happy with the suggested outcome, how likely are you to reach agreement during the meeting?

Very unlikely	**A** B C D E	Very likely

Do not reach agreement unless you are happy with the terms. You can reconvene at a later date if you are not happy.

13 As you work to reach agreement, who should normally sum up what has been agreed along the way?

You	A B C D E	The other party

Make certain that you sum up what has been agreed as you work through the negotiation. This helps keep track of progress.

14 What should you do when you are in a negotiation and you don't understand something?

Ask questions to clarify the matter	A B C D E	Let the matter pass without saying anything

Always ask if you are uncertain about what has been said.

15 What should you do when you are in a negotiation and the other party will not give anything away?

Feel that you've reached a stalemate and give up	A B C D **E**	**Ask questions and explore possibilities**

Do not give up if the other party will not give in. Summarise the issues/areas where you have reached agreement. Ask questions and invent options.

16 What should an effective negotiator's attitude be towards conflict in a negotiation?

Prefer to avoid conflict	A B C D **E**	**Conflict is healthy and should be aired**

Do not expect not to encounter conflict in negotiations. It is healthy and it should be aired.

17 How and when should you make concessions during a negotiation?

Make the concession early on in the negotiation	A B C D **E**	**Make the concession slowly and make it look more significant than it is**

Do not make concessions too early in a negotiation. Make them slowly and make them seem as though you are giving away more than you are.

18 When should you raise important issues during a negotiation?

Early on in the negotiation	A B C D E	Towards the end of the negotiation

Raise important issues early on in a negotiation while you are still fresh.

19 With whom should you feel happier negotiating?

Someone on the same level as you	A B C D E	Anyone, irrespective of title or position

If you have done your preparation, you should feel happy to negotiate with anyone at any level.

20 How often should you invent options/new ideas in negotiations?

Frequently	A B C D E	Rarely

By inventing options and putting forward new ideas you move the negotiation forward.

Recommended reading

Cohen, Steve (2002) *Negotiation Skills for Managers (A Briefcase Book)*, McGraw-Hill, Maidenhead.

30
One-to-one training

This quiz is designed as a self-assessment tool to be used after one-to-one training has taken place, either at work or after a practice session.

One-to-one training

Provide examples of what you did following one-to-one training in the areas below:

1 How did you prepare for the one-to-one training?

2 How did you put the training into context?

3 How did you set the scene with the learner? What did you tell them about the task and the training time involved?

4 Did you explain the training in a logical order?

5 Did you start with the easiest part first?

6 How did you break the training into digestible sections?

7 How did you bring out key learning points?

8 How did you maintain the learner's interest and motivation to learn?

9 How did you get the learner to participate?

10 What practical application of the training did you allow the learner?

11 What questions did you ask the learner to test their understanding?

12 How did the learner know how they were getting on?

13 How did you show your confidence in them?

14 How did you ensure that the learner's performance met the required standard?

15 What steps will you next take to further develop the learner in this area?

Recommended reading

Buckley, Roger and Caple, Jim (1996) *One to One Training and Coaching Skills (Practical Trainer Series)*, Kogan Page, London.

31
Performance appraisal

This quiz allows individuals to test their knowledge of best practice in appraisal.

Performance appraisal

Tick the reply that you consider appropriate:

1 As the appraiser, should you know the outcome of the appraisal before the performance interview takes place?

Yes ____   No ____

2 Which of the following do you believe best describes an appraisal?

A joint exchange of views ____
An opportunity for the appraisee to have their say ____
An opportunity for the appraiser to tell the appraisee how they are doing ____

3 Who should do more of the talking during the appraisal?

You ____   The appraisee ____   Equal share ____

4 How frequently should you ask the person you are appraising their opinions during the appraisal?

Often ____   Sometimes ____   Seldom ____   Never ____

5 Which of the following skills is the appraiser likely to use LEAST during an appraisal?

Listening skills ____
Feedback skills ____
Questioning skills ____
Counselling skills ____

6 Which of the following statements are NOT appropriate feedback during an appraisal?

'You have a very argumentative personality'
'Everything's fine. You're doing great'.
'I particularly appreciate the time you took to complete the report. It meant that we had the information within the week.'

7 Where should the emphasis of the appraisal be?

Looking backwards at past performance
Looking forward to the future
Both looking backwards and looking forwards

8 Who should set objectives for the future?

The appraiser   ——

The appraisee   ——

The appraiser and the appraisee jointly   ——

9 Which of the following statements BEST describes how the appraisee should feel at the end of the appraisal?

Happy with their performance   ——

Aware of what they have done well and areas where they need
   to improve   ——

Unhappy with their performance   ——

10 When should the appraisee's objectives be reviewed after the appraisal?

At the next appraisal   ——

Every month   ——

Every two months   ——

Every six months   ——

Suggested answers

1 As the appraiser, should you know the outcome of the appraisal before the performance interview takes place?

No, you should not pre-empt the outcome of the appraisal

2 Which of the following do you believe best describes an appraisal?

A joint exchange of views

3 Who should do more of the talking during the appraisal?

The appraisee

4 How frequently should you ask the person you are appraising their opinions during the appraisal?

Often – this is the appraisee's opportunity to state their opinions

5 Which of the following skills is the appraiser likely to use LEAST during an appraisal?

Counselling skills

6 Which of the following statements are NOT appropriate feedback during an appraisal?

'You have a very argumentative personality': it is not appropriate to give feedback on personality rather than behaviour
'Everything's fine. You're doing great': this statement needs to be qualified by specific evidence

7 Where should the emphasis of the appraisal be?

Both looking backwards and looking forwards

8 Who should set objectives for the future?

The appraiser and the appraisee jointly

9 Which of the following statements BEST describes how the appraisee should feel at the end of the appraisal?

Aware of what they have done well and areas where they need to improve

10 When should the appraisee's objectives be reviewed after the appraisal?

Best practice is to hold a review of objectives at least every six months

Recommended reading

Ash, Eve and Quarry, Peter (1999) *The Performance Management Skills Indicator*, Gower Publishing, Aldershot.

Bacal, Robert (1998) *Performance Management (A Briefcase Book)*, McGraw-Hill, Maidenhead.

Hill, Jenny (1997) *Managing Performance*, Gower Publishing, Aldershot.

32
Performance appraisal — before, during and after

This quiz is designed to help people think through what needs to happen before, during and after a performance appraisal.

Performance appraisal — before, during and after

Listed below are descriptions that need to take place BEFORE, DURING and AFTER a performance appraisal either from the appraisee's perspective, or from the appraiser's.

Look at the descriptions and identify:

- What is MISSING from the list
- What should NOT be on the list

Preparation

The appraisee

- Be familiar with the appraisal system, the forms and the information used
- Refer to your last appraisal
- Think about your main strengths and limitations
- Think about your relationship with your boss; identify what you would like them to continue doing, start doing, stop doing

The appraiser

- Allow enough time for the appraisal
- Be familiar with the appraisal system, the forms and how the information will be used
- Book a whole day to conduct appraisals
- Refer to the person's last appraisal and to their job history
- Meet with other managers to talk about the person's performance
- Review the appraisee's key objectives, to what extent they have been achieved
- Make a judgement about reasons for under- or over-achievement of objectives
- Think about the appraisee's main strengths and limitations
- Consider what could be done by you, the appraisee or some other person to improve performance in the future
- Consider what you expect to be the outcome of the appraisal discussion

Briefing the appraisee

- Give 2 to 3 days' notice
- Explain the purpose of the appraisal
- Emphasise that it is a two-way discussion, not an inquisition
- Issue a copy of the individual's performance objectives
- Explain the structure of the discussion

During the appraisal

- Consider location, seating, layout of room in order to create a relaxed and unhurried atmosphere
- Explain the structure of the discussion
- Explain that the main emphasis of the discussion will be on the appraisee's past performance
- Encourage the appraisee to express their views through the use of open questions
- In an effective appraisal discussion the appraisee should have 60% of the airtime
- Work to a clear structure
- Use praise to build confidence
- Invite self-appraisal
- Discuss performance, not personality
- Focus on facts
- Invite suggestions from the appraisee on how to improve
- Agree measurable targets

After the appraisal

- Fill in the appraisal forms and file them

Suggested answers

Preparation

The appraisee

MISSING FROM THE LIST

- Review to what extent key objectives have been achieved and reasons for any under- or over-achievement
- Think about the next six months

    - how to improve your performance
    - problems and opportunities for the next six months
    - training and development needs
    - career opportunities
    - what help you will need

The appraiser

SHOULD NOT BE ON THE LIST

- Do **not** spend a whole day conducting appraisals
- Do not make a judgement before the appraisal about reasons for under- or over-achievement of objectives – Consider whether the successes and difficulties have been to do with the situation or the appraisee

MISSING FROM THE LIST

- Think about the appraisee's main strengths and limitations
- Identify problems and opportunities for the future
- Consider training and development needs
- Consider career opportunities

Briefing the appraisee

SHOULD NOT BE ON THE LIST

- Give 2 to 3 days' notice – The appraisee should be given at least 7 to 10 days' notice

MISSING FROM THE LIST

- Explain what needs to be prepared

During the appraisal

SHOULD NOT BE ON THE LIST

Explain that the main emphasis of the discussion will be on the appraisee's past performance – No, the emphasis should be equally on the future

MISSING FROM THE LIST

- Avoid noise/disturbances, telephone calls, interruptions
- Don't pre-judge the outcome of the interview
- Give specific examples
- There should be no surprises
- Leave the appraisee motivated and clear about areas for improvement

After the appraisal

MISSING FROM THE LIST

- Monitor and regularly review the appraisee's progress
- Help the appraisee to achieve their development plan
- Seek opportunities to give motivational feedback where performance has improved
- Discuss reasons for continuing poor performance and agree improvement plans

33
Presentation skills

This quiz will help individuals test their understanding of the most effective way to present information.

Presentation skills

Select the correct statement/s from the following:

1 When presenting, the audience's attention is greatest:

   a) At the beginning of the presentation
   b) In the middle of the presentation
   c) At the end of the presentation
   d) At the beginning and the end of the presentation

2 The audience takes the following length of time to assess whether the presenter is worth listening to:

   a) 90 seconds
   b) 5 minutes
   c) 10 minutes
   d) 30 minutes

3 When presenting it is best to tell a joke within the introduction:

   a) Yes
   b) No

4 When presenting from Powerpoint, it is best to spend most of the time:

   a) Looking at the screen
   b) Looking at the audience
   c) Looking at your notes

5 When presenting you should:

   a) Keep your hands at your sides
   b) Keep your hands behind your back
   c) Use your hands to emphasise points

6 A presenter's introduction should contain:

   a) A welcome
   b) An introduction to the presenters
   c) The objectives of the presentation
   d) The detailed background to the presentation
   e) An overview of what the presentation will cover
   f) How long the presentation should last
   g) When the audience can ask questions

7 A presenter's summary should contain:

a) A review of the objectives of the presentation
b) A summary of what has been covered
c) A call to action
d) An opportunity for questions

8 Which people in your audience are you least likely to make eye contact with?

a) The person who is the key decision maker
b) The people on either side of you
c) The person who is least influential in the room

9 What should you do to overcome nerves?

a) Drink lots of coffee
b) Practise your presentation
c) Think positively: this will be a good presentation
d) Take deep breaths to calm your nerves

10 Which part of your presentation do you need to know the best?

a) All of it
b) The beginning
c) The middle
d) The end

11 What should you do if someone asks you a question and you're not sure of the answer?

a) Ask them to repeat the question
b) Tell them that you don't know the answer
c) Make something up
d) Tell them that you can find out the answer and get back to them

Suggested answers

1 When presenting, the audience's attention is greatest:

    d) At the beginning and the end of the presentation

The audience's attention is lowest during the middle part of the presentation.

2 The audience takes the following length of time to assess whether the presenter is worth listening to:

    a) 90 seconds

It only takes 90 seconds for the audience to assess the credibility of the speaker.

3 When presenting it is best to tell a joke within the introduction:

    b) No

Not necessarily. It is essential to create rapport with the audience but this does not necessarily mean telling a joke.

4 When presenting from Powerpoint, it is best to spend most of the time:

    b) Looking at the audience

Resist the temptation to look at the screen or to keep looking down at your notes.

5 When presenting you should:

    c) Use your hands to emphasise points

Animation through body language engages the audience.

6 A presenter's introduction should contain:

    a) A welcome
    b) An introduction to the presenters
    c) The objectives of the presentation
    e) An overview of what the presentation will cover
    f) How long the presentation should last
    g) When the audience can ask questions

A detailed background to the presentation does not need to be included in the introduction.

7 A presenter's summary should contain:

    b) A summary of what has been covered
    c) A call to action
    d) An opportunity for questions

A review of the objectives of the presentation is optional.

8 Which people in your audience are you least likely to make eye contact with?

b) The people on either side of you

Often called 'orphans', presenters need to make a conscious effort to make eye contact with these people.

9 What should you do to overcome nerves?

b) Practise your presentation
c) Think positively: this will be a good presentation
d) Take deep breaths to calm your nerves

These are all techniques to help you calm your nerves.

10 Which part of your presentation do you need to know the best?

b) The beginning

This will help increase your confidence and make a good impression with your audience.

11 What should you do if someone asks you a question and you're not sure of the answer?

a) Ask them to repeat the question – this gives you time to think
d) Tell them that you can find out the answer and get back to them – this appears more positive than saying you don't know

Recommended reading

Ash, Eve and Quarry, Peter, (1999) *Presentation Effectiveness Skills Indicator*, Gower Publishing, Aldershot.

Bradbury, Andrew (2000) *Successful Presentation Skills*, Kogan Page, London.

Gilchrist, David and Davies, Rex (1996) *Wrong Presentation*, Gower Publishing, Aldershot.

34
Project management

Many terms are used in project management. This quiz is designed to test individuals' understanding of project management terms and definitions.

Project management

Below are a number of terms currently used in project management. Match the term to the definition.

1 Project	A Sequence of activities through a project which have no slack
2 Task	B The extra time available to complete a task without delaying the start of subsequent activities
3 Parallel task	C The earliest date a task can start
4 Dependent task	D The latest date a task can start without delaying the start of subsequent activities
5 Lag	E A task that cannot begin until its predecessor activity/ies are completed
6 Critical path	F Anything – people, machines, materials, money – required for completion of the project
7 Earliest start	G A group of related activities organised in a manner to accomplish a given goal
8 Latest start	H A task which can be done during the same time-frame as one or other more activities
9 Slack	I An element of work
10 Resource	J The hierarchy or levels of tasks within a project
11 Work breakdown structure	K The time delay between one task relative to another

Suggested answers

1 Project	G	A group of related activities organised in a manner to accomplish a given goal
2 Task	I	An element of work
3 Parallel task	H	A task which can be done during the same time-frame as one or other more activities
4 Dependent task	E	A task that cannot begin until its predecessor activity/ies are completed
5 Lag	K	The time delay between one task relative to another
6 Critical path	A	Sequence of activities through a project which have no slack
7 Earliest start	C	The earliest date a task can start
8 Latest start	D	The latest date a task can start without delaying the start of subsequent activities
9 Slack	B	The extra time available to complete a task without delaying the start of subsequent activities
10 Resource	F	Anything – people, machines, materials, money – required for completion of the project
11 Work breakdown structure	J	The hierarchy or levels of tasks within a project

Recommended reading

Applegarth, Mike and Posner, Keith (1998) *The Project Management Pocketbook*, Management Pocketbooks, Alresford.

Lock, Denis (2001) *Essentials of Project Management*, second edition, Gower Publishing, Aldershot.

35
Questioning skills

Use this questionnaire to help individuals distinguish between different question types.

Questioning skills

Look at the following questions and decide whether each one is an example of:

- Open
- Probing
- Closed
- Limiting
- Leading

question types.

Question	Question type
How can we get this done?	
What made you say that?	
You do want to go today, don't you?	
Do you want to pay by cheque or by credit card?	
Shall I post it to you?	
I'll come back to you later today. Is that OK?	
Shall I wrap it for you or would you like to do it?	
What reasons did he give for not turning up?	
You said you had some experience. When did you work in this area?	
Who is the best person to speak to?	
Where is the carpet department?	
You said you were unhappy. Why was that?	
You have got your money with you, haven't you?	
Would you like tea or coffee?	
Tell me why you selected this one?	
We will go together, won't we?	
Have you the correct change?	
Is your name Sylvia?	
Is it red or green?	
You will do that for me, won't you?	

COMPENDIUM OF LEARNING AND DEVELOPMENT QUIZZES

Suggested answers

Question	Question type
How can we get this done?	Open
What made you say that?	Probing
You do want to go today, don't you?	Leading
Do you want to pay by cheque or by credit card?	Limiting
Shall I post it to you?	Closed
I'll come back to you later today. Is that OK?	Closed
Shall I wrap it for you or would you like to do it?	Limiting
What reasons did he give for not turning up?	Open
You said you had some experience. When did you work in this area?	Probing
Who is the best person to speak to?	Open
Where is the carpet department?	Open
You said you were unhappy. Why was that?	Probing
You have got your money with you, haven't you?	Leading
Would you like tea or coffee?	Limiting
Tell me why you selected this one?	Probing
We will go together, won't we?	Leading
Have you the correct change?	Closed
Is your name Sylvia?	Closed
Is it red or green?	Limiting
You will do that for me, won't you?	Leading

Closed questions

A closed question is one that can be answered 'Yes' or 'No', such as

'Did you sleep well last night?'
'Did you have a good weekend?'
'Have you finished the schedules for next week?'
'Are you happy to take on that role?'

Advantages

- Puts the person at ease at the initial stages of the conversation
- Puts you in control of the situation
- Helps to obtain specific facts quickly
- Useful for 'testing understanding' and 'summarising'
- Allows you to get agreement

Open questions

An open question allows you to receive more information than a closed question. Open questions start with: What, Why, How, When, Tell me, Explain

For example:

'Tell me more about what happened?'
'What are your personal views on this idea?'
'How do you think that might work in reality?'
'Explain exactly what happened when you saw him.'

Open questions also allow you to probe for more information. Probing questions are a type of open question.

For example:

'What would be the outcome if you did that?'
'Why do you say that?'
'What makes you believe that would happen?'
'How do you mean?'
'I didn't understand that last point, can you explain it again?'

Advantages

- Useful to establish all the facts
- Allows people to express their views
- Builds rapport and shows you are interested
- Probing questions allow you to clarify your understanding

Limiting questions

A limiting question is one that gives the recipient some choice, such as
'What would you like to do first – the filing or the telephone calls?'

Advantage

* Useful to gain agreement and when time is short

Leading questions

A leading question is when the answer is in the question, such as
'You are going to send out those tickets today, aren't you?'

Advantage

* Useful for gaining clarity and understanding

36
Recruitment and equal opportunities

This quiz is intended to test an individual's knowledge of equal opportunities in relation to recruitment.

The quiz was written in 2003 and is based on the current legislation laid down in the Sex Discrimination Act 1975 and the Disability Discrimination Act 1995 as well as the codes of practice from the Equal Opportunities Commission and the Commission for Racial Equality.

N.B. As employment legislation is often changing, please check that these statutes are still in effect before using the quiz.

Recruitment and equal opportunities

Look at the following statements and decide which are true and which are false:

1 The Sex Discrimination Act 1975 (SDA) prohibits sex discrimination against individuals in the areas of employment, education and the provision and services and in the disposal or management of premises.

2 The SDA applies to women and men of any age, excluding children.

3 Anyone can take action against advertisers who place discriminatory adverts.

4 Two of the main exceptions to the Sex Discrimination Act are:

- When a charity is providing a benefit to one sex only, in accordance with its charitable instrument
- When people are competing in a sport in which the average woman is at a disadvantage to the average man because of physical strength, stamina or physique

5 The SDA applies only to England and Wales.

6 It is not direct sexual discrimination to treat a woman adversely because she is pregnant.

7 It is indirect sex discrimination against men to include in an advert a requirement to be under 5′ 10″ (1.78m).

8 Sex discrimination is lawful in recruitment if the job needs to be held by a man to preserve privacy and decency.

9 Age limits should be included in recruitment only if they are necessary for the job. An unjustifiable age limit could constitute indirect discrimination, for example against women who have taken time out of employment to have a family.

10 Recruitment solely or primarily by word of mouth should be avoided in a workforce predominantly of one sex, if in practice it prevents members of the opposite sex applying.

11 Where organisations wish to encourage members of one sex to apply for jobs as they are under-represented currently, it is lawful to withhold recruitment information from one sex in an attempt to encourage applications from the opposite sex.

12 An advertisement that uses a job description with a sexual connotation, such as 'waiter', 'salesgirl', etc., is not taken as an intention to commit an unlawful discriminatory act.

13 The Disability Discrimination Act 1995 states that it is unlawful for an employer to discriminate against a disabled person:

a) in the arrangements which he makes for the purpose of determining to whom he should offer employment;

b) in the terms on which he offers that person employment; or

c) by refusing to offer, or deliberately not offering, him employment.

14 There is no statutory requirement to take up references, arrange medicals, prepare job descriptions, prepare person specifications or check qualifications.

15 Employers should not confine advertisements unjustifiably to those areas of publications which would exclude or disproportionately reduce the numbers of applicants of a particular racial group.

16 Employers should avoid prescribing requirements such as length of residence or experience in the UK. Where a particular qualification is required, it should be made clear that a fully comparable qualification obtained overseas is as acceptable as a UK qualification.

17 Any decision not to make an offer of employment must not be based on sex, marital status, ethnic background or ethnicity.

18 Criminal offences can be taken into account during the recruitment process.

19 Overseas workers can be employed without the issue of a work permit.

20 You can refuse a person's employment on the grounds of membership or non-membership of a trade union.

Suggested answers

1 The Sex Discrimination Act 1975 (SDA) prohibits sex discrimination against individuals in the areas of employment, education and the provision and services and in the disposal or management of premises: **True**.

2 The SDA applies to women and men of any age, excluding children: **False**. The SDA applies to women and men of any age, including children.

3 Anyone can take action against advertisers who place discriminatory adverts: **False**. Only the Equal Opportunities Commission can take action against advertisers.

4 Two of the main exceptions to the Sex Discrimination Act are:

- When a charity is providing a benefit to one sex only, in accordance with its charitable instrument
- When people are competing in a sport in which the average woman is at a disadvantage to the average man because of physical strength, stamina or physique: **True**.

5 The SDA applies only to England and Wales: **False**. The SDA applies to England, Wales and Scotland.

6 It is not direct sexual discrimination to treat a woman adversely because she is pregnant: **False**. It is direct sexual discrimination.

7 It is indirect sex discrimination against men to include in an advert a requirement to be under 5′ 10″. **True**, if this is not justifiable.

8 Sex discrimination is lawful in recruitment if the job needs to be held by a man to preserve privacy and decency: **True**.

9 Age limits should be included in recruitment only if they are necessary for the job. An unjustifiable age limit could constitute indirect discrimination, for example against women who have taken time out of employment to have a family: **True**.

10 Recruitment solely or primarily by word of mouth should be avoided in a workforce predominantly of one sex, if in practice it prevents members of the opposite sex applying: **True**.

11 Where organisations wish to encourage members of one sex to apply for jobs as they are under-represented currently, it is lawful to withhold recruitment information from one sex in an attempt to encourage applications from the opposite sex: **False**. It is unlawful.

12 An advertisement that uses a job description with a sexual connotation, such as 'waiter', 'salesgirl', etc., is not taken as an intention to commit an unlawful discriminatory act: **False**. It is unlawful unless the advertisement states that the job is open to men and women or uses descriptions applying to both sexes (e.g. 'waiter' or 'waitress').

13 The Disability Discrimination Act 1995 states that it is unlawful for an employer to discriminate against a disabled person:

   a) in the arrangements which he makes for the purpose of determining to whom he should offer employment;
   a) in the terms on which he offers that person employment; or
   a) by refusing to offer, or deliberately not offering, him employment: **All True**.

14 There is no statutory requirement to take up references, arrange medicals, prepare job descriptions, prepare person specifications or check qualifications: **True**.

15 Employers should not confine advertisements unjustifiably to those areas of publications which would exclude or disproportionately reduce the numbers of applicants of a particular racial group: **True**.

16 Employers should avoid prescribing requirements such as length of residence or experience in the UK. Where a particular qualification is required it should be made clear that a fully comparable qualification obtained overseas is as acceptable as a UK qualification obtained overseas is as acceptable as a UK qualification: **True**.

17 Any decision not to make an offer of employment must not be based on sex, marital status, ethnic background or ethnicity: **True**.

18 Criminal offences can be taken into account during the recruitment process: **False**. Criminal offences are not to be taken into account where they are time-lapsed and where the applicant will not fall into one of the employment categories exempted from the provisions of the Rehabilitation of Offenders Act 1974.

19 Overseas workers can be employed without the issue of a work permit. **False**. Overseas workers, except EU nationals and certain others, can be employed only after the issue of a work permit.

20 You can refuse a person's employment on the grounds of membership or non-membership of a trade union. **False**.

Recommended websites

Commission for Racial Equality (www.cre.gov.uk).
Equal Opportunities Commission (www.eco.org.uk).

37
Recruitment interviewing

This quiz allows people to assess their understanding of best practice in recruitment interviewing.

Recruitment interviewing

Answer the following questions:

1 An outline of the duties, responsibilities and conditions of a job is called

_____

2 A report describing the essential and desired skills, qualities and experience of the person required for a particular job is called

_____

3 A document containing the candidate's work history, skills, achievements and capabilities is called

_____

4 The pre-interview process of eliminating those candidates who do not meet the criteria you have drawn up is called

_____

5 The discussion to measure the candidate's qualities and abilities against the set criteria and allow the candidate to find out about the organisation is called

_____

6 The selection of questions related to key criteria used during the interview (which take into account what will be particularly important in the role) is called

_____

7 Which of the following should you not do at the beginning of a recruitment interview and why:

- Thank the interviewee for coming to the interview
- Introduce yourself and the other interviewer/s and your roles
- Ask the candidate how they like to be addressed
- Offer the interviewee refreshments
- Explain the interview structure
- Explain why you will be taking notes during the course of the interview
- Start the interview with a difficult question

8 What two types of questions should you use most during the interview?

_____

9 Why should you ask only one question at a time as an interviewer?

_____

10 Why should you use experience based questions (Describe a time when ....), rather than hypothetical questions (What would you do if ....)?

_____

11 Why should you make sure the candidate is not facing a window during the interview?

_____

12 Why should you ensure you ask all candidates the same type of questions during the interview?

_____

13 What should you do if the candidate is unable to answer the question?

_____

14 What should you do if the candidate will not stop talking?

_____

Suggested answers

1 An outline of the duties, responsibilities and conditions of a job is called

A job description

2 A report describing the essential and desired skills, qualities and experience of the person required for a particular job is called

A person specification

3 A document containing the candidate's work history, skills, achievements and capabilities is called

A CV

4 The pre-interview process of eliminating those candidates who do not meet the criteria you have drawn up is called

Paper screening

5 The discussion to measure the candidate's qualities and abilities against the set criteria and allow the candidate to find out about the organisation is called

A selection interview

6 The selection of questions related to key criteria used during the interview (which take into account what will be particularly important in the role) is called

The questions bank

7 Which of the following should you not do at the beginning of a recruitment interview and why:

- **Start the interview with a difficult question**
- **Start with an easy question to create a relaxed environment**

8 What two types of questions should you use most during the interview?

Open and probing

9 Why should you ask only one question at a time as an interviewer?

Multiple questions confuse the interviewee

10 Why should you use experience based questions (Describe a time when ....), rather than hypothetical questions (What would you do if ....)?

Candidates will be able to give a much more accurate account of their performance in given situations if a question asks them to relate to past experience rather than to some hypothetical future occurrence

11 Why should you make sure the candidate is not facing a window during the interview?

If the candidate is facing the window it can be distracting for them

12 Why should you ensure you ask all candidates the same type of questions during the interview?

To ensure consistency and fairness and to ensure you make meaningful comparisons

13 What should you do if the candidate is unable to answer the question?

- **Say to them 'Don't worry, take your time to answer.' Sit quietly and wait**
- **If they are seriously stumped, move onto another topic and come back to this one later to avoid pressure building up**

14 What should you do if the candidate will not stop talking?

- **Break eye contact**
- **Use body language – put your hand up and say 'Can I stop you there?'**
- **Give clues in your questions – 'Can you give me a brief account of . . .?'**

Recommended reading

Wood, Robert and Payne, Tim (1998) *Competency-based Recruitment and Selection: A Practical Guide (Strategic Human Resource Management)*, John Wiley and Sons Ltd, London.
Maitland, Iain (1991) *How to Recruit*, Gower Publishing, Aldershot.

38
Recruitment and selection

This quiz invites individuals to identify the correct steps in the recruitment and selection process.

Recruitment and selection

Place the following steps in the selection and recruitment schedule in the correct order:

Activity
Inform the unsuccessful candidates
Review/write Person Specification
Send out job details and application form. Request CV
Induction
Paper screen to draw up shortlist
Offer feedback to all candidates
Send out rejections/invitations for first selection stage
Carry out interview and/or other selection methods
Make offer to successful candidate(s)
Advertise (where will you advertise/publicise the job and how will it appear?)
Agree start date
Review/write Job Description
Make decision
Decide on selection methods
Agree application deadline

Suggested answers

Activity
1 Review/write Job Description
2 Review/write Person Specification
3 Decide on selection methods
4 Advertise (where will you advertise/publicise the job and how will it appear?)
5 Send out job details and application form. Request CV
6 Agree application deadline
7 Paper screen to draw up shortlist
8 Send out rejections/invitations for first selection stage
9 Carry out interview and/or other selection methods
10 Make decision
11 Make offer to successful candidate(s)
12 Inform the unsuccessful candidates
13 Offer feedback to all candidates
14 Agree start date
15 Induction

Recommended reading

Wood, Robert and Payne, Tim (1998) *Competency-based Recruitment and Selection: A Practical Guide (Strategic Human Resource Management)*, John Wiley and Sons Ltd, London.

39
SMART objectives

This quiz can be used to help people identify SMART objectives.

SMART objectives

Which of these objects is SMART?

1 Additional training on general issues

2 Reduce the cost of photocopying by 31 December

3 Be more willing to make presentations

4 Learn to look back and consider the bigger picture

5 Gain understanding of the customer database

6 Continue to provide a first-class level of customer service

7 Hold a progress meeting with all the team in order to delegate work appropriately

8 Ensure that 100% of managers receive performance management training by December this year

9 Achieve £100,000 of new business from new customers by 31 December this year

10 Maintain quality standards

Answer

SMART =

SPECIFIC: spelling out exactly what the individual needs to achieve

MEASURABLE: so that when the objective is reviewed you have criteria that will help you decide whether the individual has achieved the objective

ACHIEVABLE: stretching and challenging for the individual but still within an individual's capabilities and control

RELEVANT: to the needs of the individual, the team and the organisation

TIME-BOUND: with target dates for completion of each objective

Therefore only statements 8 and 9 are SMART

Recommended reading

Bacal, Robert (1998) *Performance Management (A Briefcase Book)* McGraw-Hill, Maidenhead.

40
Stress management

This quiz is designed to help individuals recognise the symptoms of stress in themselves and others as well as the most common causes of stress.

Recognising the symptoms of stress

Here is a list of behaviours that you or others may display. Identify which are symptoms of stress:

- Poor concentration
- Confusion
- Lack of awareness
- Poor planning
- Not completing tasks
- Indecisiveness
- Feeling achy
- Fatigue
- Poor posture
- Rapid breathing
- Tight chest
- Indigestion
- Stomach cramps
- Shoulder and neck pain
- Headaches
- Dilated pupils
- Sweating
- Dropping things
- Forgetting things
- Biting nails, lip or cheek
- Wanting more time to yourself
- Eating too little
- Eating too much
- Smoking more
- Drinking more alcohol
- Taking un-prescribed drugs
- Feeling sick
- Expecting yourself to do more/better
- Being irritable
- Having minor accidents
- Feeling angry, hurt, worried, unhappy
- Feeling tense

Recognising the most common causes of stress

Here is a list of the most common causes of stress. Place these in an order of likelihood to cause stress:

- Lack of time
- Boredom
- Moving home
- Financial worries
- Family pressures
- Change
- Low self-image
- Illness
- Crisis in a relationship
- Losing a loved one
- Frustrations at work
- Fighting bureaucracy
- Unemployment
- Environmental ill-health
- Caring for others

Suggested answers

Symptoms of stress

All the items on the list are symptoms of stress if they happen repeatedly.

Common causes of stress

The most common causes of stress in order are:

1 Losing a loved one

2 Moving home

3 Financial worries

4 Crisis in a relationship

5 Family pressures

6 Illness

7 Unemployment

8 Lack of time

9 Boredom

10 Frustrations at work

11 Fighting bureaucracy

12 Environmental ill-health

13 Caring for others

14 Change

15 Low self-image

Recommended reading

James, Judi (1998) *More Time, Less Stress*, Piatkus Books, London.
Priest, Simon and Welch, Jon (1998) *Creating a Stress-free Office*, Gower Publishing, Aldershot.

41
Team work

Use this quiz to help team members increase their understanding of each other.

Team work

Answer the following questions in relation to your team. Then compare your responses to those of your fellow team members.

1 How would you describe the role of your team?

2 What are the objectives of your team?

3 Who in the team lives the furthest from your place of work?

4 Who in the team is the best time-manager?

5 Who in the team is the most customer focused?

6 What have been the greatest achievements of the team in the past six months?

7 What have been the biggest disappointments for the team in the past six months?

8 Who in the team is the liveliest?

9 How could communication in the team be improved?

10 Who in the team is most supportive?

11 Where is there duplication of roles and responsibilities in the team?

12 What is the team's approach to conflict and disagreement?

13 Who is the best listener in the team?

14 What is the biggest challenge for the team in the next six months?

15 What would you like to improve in order for the team to work more effectively together?

42
Telephone skills

This quiz is designed to help people identify best practice on the telephone.

Telephone skills

Look at the following situations and assess which option represents best practice on the telephone:

1 When you are listening to someone who is talking at length on the telephone, should you:

   a) listen actively and make notes to record what they are saying?
   b) look through other papers on your desk as you are listening?
   c) doodle or mentally 'switch off'?

2 You receive a call from someone complaining about an area in which you have no involvement. Should you:

   a) say it is nothing to do with you, the caller will have to contact the correct person to complain?
   b) empathise with the caller about the problem, collect the facts and offer to ring back with an answer?
   c) transfer the caller to the correct extension?

3 You need to pass on an urgent and lengthy message to someone in another department. When you call their extension you reach their voice-mail. Should you:

   a) put the phone down and say you'll try again later?
   b) leave the whole of the lengthy message?
   c) leave a short message asking the person to phone you, briefly explaining the reason why?

4 You have an important task which needs to be completed without interruptions. Should you:

   a) make arrangements for someone else to take your calls?
   b) put on your answer-machine or use voice-mail?
   c) leave the phone ringing for a while and then answer it?

5 You receive a call from an irate customer who is very upset because an important letter you sent has not arrived. The customer is very aggressive to you on the phone. Should you:

   a) ask for the customer's name, then try and establish the facts?
   b) become aggressive back to the customer?
   c) apologise then find out the facts?

6 You are passing an absent colleague's desk and the phone rings. Should you:

  a) answer the call and take a message?
  b) pick up the phone, explain that no one is there, and ask the caller to ring back later?
  c) let the phone ring as you know that eventually the call will go back to the switchboard?

7 You are deep in discussion with a customer on the telephone when a colleague comes in to the room and interrupts you. Should you:

  a) ignore the interruption and continue listening to the customer?
  b) put your hand over the mouthpiece and say you will not be long?
  c) interrupt the customer and say you need to speak briefly to your colleague?

8 When you answer the phone, should you:

  a) give the name of your department?
  b) give a greeting, say your name and department?
  c) give your name?

9 When someone phones you to try to sell something, should you:

  a) tell them to go away, stop bothering you?
  b) say you'll think about it?
  c) simply say that you are not interested, thank you?

10 A caller is giving you their company address at the end of a conversation. Should you:

  a) repeat each part of the address?
  b) make listening noises – uh huh, etc.?
  c) let the caller speak?

When you have finished, turn to the answers page and award yourself 3 points for each correct answer. Then add up your total.

Suggested answers

1 When you are listening to someone who is talking at length on the telephone, you should:

   a) listen actively and make notes to record what they are saying

2 You receive a call from someone complaining about an area in which you have no involvement. You should:

   b) empathise with the caller about the problem, collect the facts and offer to ring back with an answer

3 You need to pass on an urgent and lengthy message to someone in another department. When you call their extension you reach their voice-mail. You should:

   c) leave a short message asking the person to phone you, briefly explaining the reason why

4 You have an important task which needs to be completed without interruptions. You should:

   a) make arrangements for someone else to take your calls

5 You receive a call from an irate customer who is very upset because an important letter you sent has not arrived. The customer is very aggressive to you on the phone. You should:

   c) apologise then find out the facts

6 You are passing an absent colleague's desk and the phone rings. You should:

   a) answer the call and take a message

7 You are deep in discussion with a customer on the telephone when a colleague comes in to the room and interrupts you. You should:

   a) ignore the interruption and continue listening to the customer

8 When you answer the phone, you should:

   b) give a greeting, say your name and department

9 When someone phones you to try to sell something, you should:

   c) simply say that you not interested, thank you

10 A caller is giving you their company address at the end of a conversation. You should:

   a) repeat each part of the address

How to interpret your score

The maximum score possible is 30 points. The higher your score the greater your professionalism on the telephone.

21–30   You have a customer-friendly manner on the telephone. You deal with people on the telephone in an open, honest and direct manner.

15–20   Your telephone manner could be improved. You have a tendency to appear unhelpful or uninterested on the telephone.

1–14   You do not present a professional approach on the telephone. You have a tendency not to appear to be customer-friendly on the telephone.

Recommended reading

Collier Cool, Lisa (1989) *Phone Power*, Robert Hale, London.
Richards, Mary (1997) *The Telephone Skills Pocketbook*, Management Pocketbooks, Alresford.

43
Time management

This quiz is designed to allow individuals to put into practice their prioritisation skills.

Time management

The objective of this quiz is to give you the opportunity to apply your prioritisation skills and isolate areas of time management where you wish to improve.

Instructions

- Go through the time management ideas and mark those which you think you may be able to apply immediately.
- Look at the marked items and put an A to the left of the ones which appear to be the most important to you.
- Now, go back and look at the As and select the three most important ones for you. Note them A-1, A-2 and A-3.

Time management ideas

1 Assess your work – projects, tasks, in-tray post, etc., and allocate priorities.

2 Arrange and allocate your priorities into categories A, B, C and D.

3 Throw away the Ds – these are not important or urgent.

4 Keep the Cs – urgent but not important – to be actioned during non-priority time.

5 Date/time check the Bs – they are usually important but not urgent.

6 Sub-divide your As – A^1, A^2, A^3, etc.

7 Do A^1 now, then your other As – not those attractive Cs!

8 Make appointments with yourself in your diary – this is the personal time you must have during the day.

9 Stick to your plan. Make it and do it now.

10 Select your personal and workout 'best' times to get things done, and plan to do your most important work then.

11 Chop a big task down into smaller, more manageable pieces.

12 Estimate the end time for a task, not just the starting time.

13 Have a daily 'To Do' list, particularly for your A items.

14 Review the daily list each day (first thing in the morning or last thing in the evening) and plan your priorities.

15 Keep your daily 'To Do' list always in sight.

16 Don't include too many items on your 'To Do' list; remember the jobs which always crop up unexpectedly.

17 Maintain a second 'To Do' list for longer-term tasks or those to which a date cannot yet be given.

18 Transfer items from the second list to the daily list whenever relevant.

19 Write it down. Don't try to keep your 'To Do' lists in your head, keep that brainpower free to actually do them!

20 Leave time in your day for the unexpected.

21 Delegate whenever possible: down, sideways, up.

22 Delegate tasks but do not abdicate them: if it is your task, you still have the final responsibility.

23 Agree the reviews which are part of the delegation process.

24 Concentrate personally on those tasks whose success depends on you.

25 Do the unpleasant task first, or as early as possible, particularly if it is your A[1]. (It is also most people's experience that these jobs usually turn out to be less unpleasant than was anticipated.)

26 Stop being the nice guy all the time – learn to say 'NO'.

27 Set yourself personal deadlines for most tasks and stick to them if at all possible.

28 Stick at the task you know must be done.

29 Do one thing at a time.

30 Plan what you have to do, who is going to do it, how it is going to be done, where is it to be done, by when has it to be done. Why has it to be done?

Recommended reading

Gleeson, Kerry (2000) *The Personal Efficiency Program: How to Get Organized to Do More Work in Less Time*, John Wiley & Sons, London.
Woodhull, Angela V. (1997) *The New Time Manager*, Gower Publishing, Aldershot.
Ash, Eve and Quarry, Peter (1999) *Time Management Skills Indicator*, Gower Publishing, Aldershot.

44
Written communication skills

This quiz encourages people to use plain English as part of written communication.

Written communication skills

Look at the phrases below and rephrase them. Use plain English to convey what they really mean:

1 Please do not hesitate to

2 At this moment in time

3 In the normal course of our procedure

4 In the event of

5 We will endeavour to ascertain

6 We have discontinued the policy of

7 I am of the opinion that

8 I have pleasure in enclosing herewith

9 It was noted that

10 We would advise you that

11 We write in connection with your recent correspondence

12 We are unable to meet with your request

13 We trust the above clarified the matter

14 We hope that the above meets with your approval

15 We have read and noted the contents of your letter

16 We are now in receipt of your letter

17 It is with regret that

18 In the fullness of time

19 If this should materialise

20 It may necessitate

Suggested answers

1 Please do not hesitate to	Please
2 At this moment in time	Now
3 In the normal course of our procedure	Usually
4 In the event of	If
5 We will endeavour to ascertain	We will try to find out
6 We have discontinued the policy of	We no longer
7 I am of the opinion that	I think
8 I have pleasure in enclosing herewith	I enclose
9 It was noted that	I have noted your comments
10 We would advise you that	Don't use – go straight to the point
11 We write in connection with your recent correspondence	Thank you for your letter
12 We are unable to meet with your request	We cannot do what you ask
13 We trust the above clarified the matter	I hope this explains the situation
14 We hope that the above meets with your approval	I hope that this is fine by you
15 We have read and noted the contents of your letter	Thank you for your letter
16 We are now in receipt of your letter	We have received your letter
17 It is with regret that	I am sorry that
18 In the fullness of time	Eventually
19 If this should materialise	If this should happen
20 It may necessitate	We may need

Recommended reading

Cutts, Martin (1999) *Quick Reference Plain English Guide*, Oxford University Press, Oxford.